*On the Interaction
Between Atomic Nuclei
and Electrons*

A Series of Books in Physics

EDITORS: HENRY M. FOLEY AND MALVIN A. RUDERMAN

Concepts of Classical Optics
   John Strong

Thermophysics
   Allen L. King

Introduction to Electromagnetic Field and Waves
   Dale R. Corson and Paul Lorrain

Modern Quantum Theory
   Behram Kurşunoğlu

X-Ray Diffraction in Crystals, Imperfect Crystals, and Amorphous Bodies
   A. Guinier

On the Interaction Between Atomic Nuclei and Electrons (*A Golden Gate Edition*)
   H. B. G. Casimir

H. B. G. CASIMIR

Philips Research Laboratories, Eindhoven, The Netherlands

On the Interaction
Between Atomic Nuclei
and Electrons

WITH A FOREWORD BY I. I. RABI

W. H. FREEMAN AND COMPANY

SAN FRANCISCO AND LONDON

PRINTED IN THE UNITED STATES OF AMERICA
LIBRARY OF CONGRESS CATALOG CARD NUMBER 62-19662

*Originally published in 1936 by Teyler's Tweede
Genootschap, Haarlem, De Erven F. Bohn N. V.*

"Maar juist hierin is voor een deel het nut van elke
uitbreiding onzer natuurkennis gelegen,
dat zij ons duidelijker voor oogen stelt,
wat er nog te doen overblijft. . . ."

H. A. LORENTZ
Acad. Proefschrift

Preface to the Second Edition

When W. H. Freeman and Co. proposed to reissue my paper "On the Interaction Between Atomic Nuclei and Electrons" I felt a little doubt whether this publication would still serve some useful purpose. When it first appeared, this paper was in no way a complete synopsis, and today, after twenty-five years, its contents seem rather insignificant in comparison with the vast amount of experimental material and the impressive body of theory that have come into existence through the development of radio spectroscopy and nuclear-spin resonance. Perhaps, however, this very scantiness may be of some historical interest, because it reveals the speed of progress in this field. To a younger generation it may be surprising to discover how the first results on nuclear magnetic moments and electric quadrupole moments were obtained by the laborious and often rather unsatisfactory analysis of optical spectra. What is more important, however, is that recent advances in the theory of nuclear forces and in quantum electrodynamics have not led to essential modifications of the theory of hyperfine structure: the methods used in my paper for treating the interaction of electrons and nuclei and the discussion of the foundations of these methods remain substantially correct. The essential point is that the interaction between electrons and nuclei that is responsible for hyperfine structure and internal conversion is purely electromagnetic. Of course, there does exist a specific nuclear interaction that manifests itself in beta-radioactivity, but this type of interaction has no appreciable influence on the phenomena discussed here, although it does give rise to the magnetic moment of the neutron and the "anomalous" value of the magnetic moment of the proton. In my paper the attitude is taken that there might conceivably exist a nonelectromagnetic interaction proportional to the probability density of the electron at the nucleus. If the electron is described by $\psi(\mathbf{r})$, where $\mathbf{r}$ is the radius vector from the nucleus to the electron, then this interaction would be proportional to $|\psi(o)|^2$. But no evidence for this type of interaction is found. As a matter of fact, during the history of this subject there have been several occasions on which it seemed at first that the interpretation of hyperfine structure or internal conversion would require such an interaction, but more accurate analysis has shown that it can be dispensed with.

The mathematical treatment of the electromagnetic interaction given in the text is fairly straightforward, but there are one or two points that call for some additional comment.

Currents and dipoles

It is essential that the magnetic interaction between an electron and the nucleus should be treated as an interaction between currents: in this respect there is no difference between orbital moment and spin; the action of the spin cannot be described as the action of a distribution of magnetic dipoles.

The interaction may be written as $\mathbf{H}_0 \cdot \mathbf{\mu}_N$, where $\mathbf{\mu}_N$ is the nuclear magnetic moment and $\mathbf{H}_0$ is the magnetic field produced by the electrons at the nucleus, which we shall assume to be at the origin of the coordinate system. According to a naive magnetic dipole treatment, the contribution of the spin to the field $\mathbf{H}_0$ is obtained by taking the average of

$$\frac{\mathbf{\mu}_{\text{el}}}{r^3} - \frac{3\,(\mathbf{\mu}_{\text{el}} \cdot \mathbf{r})\,\mathbf{r}}{r^5}$$

over the probability density of the electron. This is perfectly correct if $|\psi(o)|^2 = 0$: there is no difference between dipoles and currents so far as the field outside the dipole or current distribution is concerned. For s-states, however, $|\psi(o)|^2 \neq 0$, and the integral has no meaning. One might assume a small region of impenatrability* around the origin, but then the interaction would depend on the shape of this region: $\mathbf{H}_0 = 0$ for a sphere; $\mathbf{H}_0 = (8\pi/3)\,(\mathbf{\mu}_{\text{el}})\,|\psi(o)|^2$ for a very flat ellipsoid perpendicular to the spin; and $\mathbf{H}_0 = -\,(4\pi/3)\,(\mathbf{\mu}_{\text{el}})\,|\psi(o)|^2$ for a needle parallel to the spin. All this is of course well known from classical electrodynamics.

The correct way to calculate $\mathbf{H}_0$ is to start from a current dis-

---

* Lewis Carroll, *Through the Looking Glass*, Chap. 6.

tribution circulating freely around the nucleus:

$$\mathbf{i} = c \operatorname{curl} (\psi^* \mathbf{u}_{el} \psi).$$

For an s-state with $\mathbf{u}_{el}$ parallel to the positive z-axis this gives

$$i_x = c \frac{e\hbar}{2mc} \frac{y}{r} \frac{d|\psi|^2}{dr},$$

$$i_y = -c \frac{e\hbar}{2mc} \frac{x}{r} \frac{d|\psi|^2}{dr},$$

$$\mathbf{H}_0 = \frac{e\hbar}{2mc} \iiint \frac{1}{r^2} \frac{d|\psi|^2}{dr} \sin^2 \vartheta \, r^2 \, dr \sin \vartheta \, d\vartheta \, d\phi$$

$$= \frac{8\pi}{3} \frac{e\hbar}{2mc} |\psi(0)|^2,$$

a formula derived by Fermi.* In the Dirac theory of the electron this treatment follows almost automatically, and in the text no further attention is given to this question, which nevertheless has occasionally given rise to confusion. Exactly the same problem turned up in the discussion of the magnetic interaction in the deuteron (Bethe and Bacher†) and the solution is entirely analogous.**

There is ample evidence, both theoretical and empirical, that the interaction is an interaction of currents. It is therefore somewhat disconcerting to find a recent text on electromagnetic theory in which the macroscopic treatment is based on the idea of magnetic dipoles.‡

Approximate character of magnetic interaction

The expression $-\mathbf{H}_0 \cdot \mathbf{u}_N$ for the interaction cannot possibly be a rigorous expression because it would lead to an infinite binding energy. This is best seen by means of a variational method. Let us set

$$\psi = \left(\frac{1}{\pi a^3} \right)^{1/2} e^{-r/a}.$$

* E. Fermi, *Z. Phys.*, **60**:320, 1930.
† H. Bethe and R. F. Bacher, *Rev. Mod. Phys.*, 8, 1936.
** H. B. G. Casimir, *Physica*, **3**:936, 1936.
‡ R. M. Fano, L. J. Chu, and R. B. Adler, *Electromagnetic Fields, Energy, and Forces*, Wiley, New York, 1960.

This leads to a kinetic energy $\hbar^2/2ma^2$, a potential energy $-Ze^2/a$, and a hyperfine coupling

$$- \mathbf{H}_0 \cdot \mathbf{\mu} = - \frac{2}{3} \frac{1}{a^3} \cdot \frac{e\hbar}{2mc} \cdot \gamma \frac{e\hbar}{2Mc},$$

where $\gamma e\hbar/2Mc$ is the magnetic moment of the nucleus. If we take a sufficiently small this last term will always dominate, but this will only occur when $a \leq e^2/Mc^2$, which is much smaller than any nuclear radius. It may be concluded that, although a Hamiltonian with an interaction term $-\mathbf{H}_0 \cdot \mathbf{\mu}_N$ has infinitely low eigenvalues, it can be used to calculate energies for any realistic wave function.

Refinements: higher moments, finite nuclear size, quantum electrodynamics

In my paper only magnetic dipoles and electric quadrupoles are treated in some detail because it seemed at the time that the effects of higher terms would be too small to be observed. The influence of a magnetic octupole moment was considered in some detail in a paper by Casimir and Karreman* (reprinted here as Appendix B), but again the conclusion was that the effect is too small to be observed. This conclusion is no longer valid; the effect is just within the scope of modern methods of radio spectroscopy.

The effect of a finite size of the nucleus on magnetic hyperfine structure is vaguely indicated in Section 2. Again, such effects are now well within the range of accuracy. They have been discussed in detail by Bohr and Weisskopf † in connection with experimental results on hydrogen and deuterium.

Since the late forties there has been considerable progress in the quantum theory of the electromagnetic field and the relativistic treatment of the two-body problem. Deviations of the energy levels of atomic hydrogen from the Sommerfeld formula (which was originally derived by applying the older methods of quantization to relativistic mechanics, but which also follows from Dirac's theory) were observed by Lamb and Retherford. In addition, a correction to the magnetic moment of the electron was found experimentally

---

* H. B. G. Casimir and C. Karreman, *Physica*, **9**:494, 1942.
† A. Bohr and V. Weisskopf, *Phys. Rev.*, **77**:94, 1950.

by Kusch. Both effects can be satisfactorily explained on the basis of quantum electrodynamics. Similar efforts must evidently exist in hyperfine structure,* but they are very small; so far their discussion has not led to any essentially new points of view.

The discussion of internal conversion is much more sketchy than that of hyperfine structure, but here also the general tenor of the argument remains valid. The rather clumsy treatment of multipole radiation originally given in Section 21 has been eliminated; this subject is now covered in Appendix A. A more elementary, and perhaps more serious, omission in my original paper is that the possible influence of the polarization of the inner core by the outer electron is not even mentioned. Of course, this effect may be regarded as a special form of configuration interaction. The influence of magnetic polarization on magnetic interaction is certainly very small, but the influence of electric polarization on electric quadrupole interaction may be appreciable.

I want to express my sincere thanks to Dr. W. J. A. Goossens, who at my request checked large sections of the calculations and corrected a number of errors and omissions. Thanks are due to M. Nijhoff, publisher at the Hague, for granting permission to reprint the material in Appendix B, and to the trustees of Teyler's Foundation at Haarlem for their cooperative attitude with respect to the republication of a paper that might never have been written but for their stimulating influence.

June 1962   H. B. G. CASIMIR

---

* R. Karplus, A. Klein and J. Schwinger, *Phys. Rev.* **84**:597, 1951.
  R. Karplus and A. Klein, *Phys. Rev.* **85**:972, 1952.

Preface to the First Edition

This paper was written as a prize essay for Teyler's Foundation at Haarlem, The Netherlands.

We have tried to give a survey of those phenomena in which the interaction between the nucleus and the electrons can be described by means of ordinary quantum mechanics, and which nevertheless depend on nuclear properties other than charge and mass.

The main part of this paper consists of a discussion of the theory of hyperfine structure; that is, the theory of the interaction of the nucleus in its stationary state with the atomic electrons. It was not our object to give a complete derivation or enumeration of all formulas that are of importance in the investigation of hyperfine structure, but we have made an attempt to analyze carefully and systematically the foundations of the theory. Details were given only where we believed that we could add something new to the existing treatment.

Our calculations are based on the assumption that the action of the nucleus on the electrons can be described as the action of a normal quantum-mechanical system, and one of the most important questions is whether this is permissible. We arrive at the result that this assumption is not necessarily correct with regard to the so-called isotope shift; moreover, in the magnetic interaction small deviations from the theory might occur. From this point of view the theory of the interaction of the electrons with the electric quadrupole moment is the most reliable part of our calculations.

In Sections 20–24 we have given a short survey of the theory of internal conversion. This theory is based on an assumption analogous to that which occurs in the theory of hyperfine structure. The last section contains some speculations on the structure of the nucleus.

The author would like to express his sincere thanks to Professor Schüler and to Dr. Schmidt in Potsdam for kindly communicating to him the results of their experiments before publication.

H. B. G. CASIMIR

Foreword

The republication of Casimir's prize essay "On the Interaction Between Atomic Nuclei and Electrons" will be very welcome to workers and to their graduate students in the fields of molecular beams, microwave and optical spectroscopy, nuclear magnetic resonance, and internal conversion.

This minor classic in the history of physics has by now served to introduce many generations of physicists to the theory of the hyperfine structure of atomic energy levels that arises from the electric and magnetic interaction of the nucleus with its orbital electrons. This new edition has been brought up to date by the inclusion of further work by the author on octupole magnetic moments of the nucleus. These small interactions have been detected experimentally with the sensitive electronic methods developed in the postwar period.

The author starts with the most elementary formulation of the problem of nucleon-electron interaction and develops the theme step by step. The reader is aware at all points of the nature of the physical assumptions and the mathematical approximations. For these reasons young workers being introduced to this field will find the book both useful and educational.

The importance and usefulness of Casimir's prize essay is attested by the numerous references one finds to it in the scientific literature, both in journals and in treatises. It is a tribute to the author's insight that after twenty-five years so few changes or additions are required to bring the treatment up to date. This essay was originally written shortly after the discovery of the nuclear electrical quadrupole moment by Schüler and Schmidt. Since that time nuclear physics has made enormous strides in accounting for nuclear magnetic and electrical moments. This field is far from exhausted, and Casimir's classic work will remain useful for a very long time.

May 1962

I. I. RABI

Contents

On the Interaction
Between Atomic Nuclei
and Electrons

1. General theory of the interaction between a nucleus in a stationary state and a number of electrons

We assume that the nucleus in its normal state has an angular momentum $i\hbar$ ($\hbar =$ Planck's constant$/2\pi$). The normal state is then $(2i + 1)$-fold degenerate; the nondegenerate states, which together form the normal state, can be described by wave functions $\varkappa_k$ ($-i \leq k \leq i$). The angular momentum (in units $\hbar$) is given by a vector operator $\mathbf{I}$ with components I_x, I_y, I_z; the components satisfy the well-known commutation relations. For a suitable choice of the $\varkappa_k$, the matrix elements are given by

$$(k|I_z|k) = k,$$

$$(k|I_x + iI_y|k - 1) = \sqrt{(i + k)(i - k + 1)}, \qquad (1.1)$$

$$(k|I_x - iI_y|k + 1) = \sqrt{(i - k)(i + k + 1)}.$$

Since all other matrix elements are zero, we have

$$I_x^2 + I_y^2 + I_z^2 = i(i + 1).$$

This relation is independent of the choice of the $\varkappa_k$.

The states of the electrons in the field of a point charge are described by wave functions ψ (n, j, m). Here j is the total angular momentum; m is the magnetic quantum number, which takes all (integral or half-integral) values between $+j$ and $-j$; and n stands for all other quantum numbers. The energy is a function of n and j; the $2j + 1$ states belonging to one and the same combination n, j are mutually degenerate. The operators of angular momentum are diagonal matrices with respect to n and j; the matrix elements for a given value of j are given by formulas exactly analogous to (1.1).

1

The states of the system nucleus plus electrons are in this approximation $(2i + 1)(2j + 1)$-fold degenerate. These states will now suffer a perturbation, the perturbation operator S being given by the difference between the true interaction and the interaction of the electrons and a point charge. Let W be the total interaction; then

$$S = W - \sum_i \frac{-Ze^2}{r_i}, \qquad (1.2)$$

where the summation is carried out over all electrons; r_i is the distance of the ith electron from the center of the nucleus, Ze the nuclear charge.

Let us assume that the separations caused by the perturbation operator S are small compared to the distances of the unperturbed energy levels (that is, the hyperfine structure is small compared to the fine structure). In this case only those matrix elements of S that are diagonal elements with respect to j and n have to be taken into account. The level with energy $E(n, j)$ is separated into a number of levels; the distances of those levels from the unperturbed level are given by the characteristic values of the matrix with elements

$$(k', m' \,|\, S \,|\, k'', m'') = \int \psi^*(n', j', m') \, \varkappa_k^*, \, S \psi(n', j', m'') \, \varkappa_{k''}.$$

Now S is invariant under simultaneous rotation of nucleus and electrons. Hence the matrix S commutes with the components of the total angular momentum. These components are given by

$$F_x = I_x + J_x,$$
$$F_y = I_y + J_y,$$
$$F_z = I_z + J_z.$$

If we transform the matrix $F^2 = F_x^2 + F_y^2 + F_z^2$ into diagonal form, by replacing the products $\psi(n, j, m) \, \varkappa_k$ by proper linear combinations of these products, then the perturbation operator will also be transformed into diagonal form, and to every characteristic value of F^2 there corresponds a characteristic value of S. The characteristic values of F^2 are equal to $f(f + 1)$, where f takes all integral (or half-integral) values between $i + j$ and $|i - j|$. A state with total angular momentum f is $(2f + 1)$-fold degenerate.

Our results may be stated more simply as follows: The existence of a nuclear angular momentum and of an interaction that is not exactly equal to the interaction of electrons and a point charge will cause a splitting of energy levels. The number of levels into which a level with electronic angular momentum j is separated can be determined with the aid of the vector model.

2. Magnetic interaction

The main part of the perturbation operator S is due to magnetic interaction. According to the general formalism of quantum mechanical perturbation theory, one can determine this interaction by calculating by means of classical electrodynamics the interaction energy of the current distribution of the electrons with the current distribution in the nucleus and taking this expression with negative sign. The appearance of this factor (-1) is connected with the well-known fact that the sum of the Hamiltonian for the motion of a particle in an exterior field and the field energy of this exterior field is not equal to the total energy of the system exterior field plus particle, but we will not dwell upon this point at present. Let $\mathbf{A}(\mathbf{r})$ be the vector potential of the field arising from the nuclear current distribution, and let $\mathbf{s}(\mathbf{r})$ be the current density of the electrons. Then the magnetic interaction energy is given by

$$S_m = -\frac{1}{c} \int (\mathbf{A} \cdot \mathbf{s}) \, d\tau. \qquad (2.1)$$

Outside the nucleus the field of the nucleus can be expanded in a series: field of a dipole, field of a quadrupole, and so on; only the first term of this series leads to an interaction energy of measurable order of magnitude.* The vector potential of a magnetic dipole can

---

*See, however, the Introduction and Appendix A.

be written in the form

$$A = \frac{\mathbf{\mu} \times \mathbf{r}}{|r|^3}.$$ (2.2)

Here μ is the dipole moment and $\mathbf{r}$ is the radius vector from the center of the nucleus to the point considered.

It follows that

$$S_m = - \frac{1}{c} \int \frac{(\mathbf{\mu} \times \mathbf{r}) \cdot \mathbf{s}}{|r|^3} \, d\tau = - \frac{1}{c} \int \mathbf{\mu} \cdot \frac{\mathbf{r} \times \mathbf{s}}{|r|^3} \, d\tau.$$

Now

$$\frac{1}{c} \int \frac{\mathbf{r} \times \mathbf{s}}{|r|^3} \, d\tau = \mathbf{H}_0,$$ (2.3)

where $\mathbf{H}_0$ is the field caused by $\mathbf{s}(\mathbf{r})$ at the point $r = 0$. Thus we find that

$$S_m = - \mathbf{\mu} \cdot \mathbf{H}_0.$$ (2.4)

One must bear in mind, however, that this expression will hold only if the part of the current distribution $\mathbf{s}$ that is lying inside the nucleus does not appreciably contribute to S_m. If this part of the current distribution gives rise to a field $\delta \mathbf{H}_0$ at $r = 0$, then S_m will differ from (2.4) by an amount of the order of magnitude $-\mathbf{\mu} \cdot \delta \mathbf{H}_0$. Only for s-electrons is $\delta \mathbf{H}_0$ not quite negligible; one finds

$$\delta H_0 / H_0 \approx \left(\frac{RZ}{a} \right)^{2\sqrt{1-Z^2a^2}-1}$$ (2.5)

(R nuclear radius, $\alpha = e^2/\hbar c = 1/137$, $a = \hbar^2/me^2 = $ radius of the first hydrogen orbit). For the heaviest nuclei this will amount to about 5%. If the magnetic moment of a nucleus is calculated from empirically determined interaction energies by means of (2.4), then errors of this order of magnitude may occur. The accuracy of such calculations is at present usually considerably less; thus it is not necessary to take these errors into account.

According to a general theorem on matrix vectors, one can always write

$$\mathbf{\mu} = \frac{e\hbar}{2mc} \frac{m}{M_p} \gamma \mathbf{I}. \tag{2.6}$$

Here m is the mass of the electrons, M_p is the mass of the proton, and γ is a numerical factor (Landé factor). The $j|j$ part of $\mathbf{H}_0$ can be written as

$$\mathbf{H}_0 = C\mathbf{J},$$

where C does not depend on the magnetic quantum number. The constant C can be determined by calculating the $m = j | m = j$ matrix element of H_z (we omit the subscript $_0$):

$$C = \frac{1}{j}(n,j,j| H_z | n,j,j)$$

or, briefly,

$$C = \frac{1}{j}\overline{(H_z)}_{m=j}.$$

We then have

$$S_m = - \frac{e\hbar}{2mc} \frac{m}{M_p} \gamma \,\overline{(H_z)}_{m=j} \frac{1}{j} (\mathbf{I}\cdot\mathbf{J}).$$

Now

$$F^2 = (\mathbf{I} + \mathbf{J})^2 = I^2 + J^2 + 2(\mathbf{I}\cdot\mathbf{J}),$$

hence

$$\mathbf{I}\cdot\mathbf{J} = \frac{1}{2}(F^2 - I^2 - J^2).$$

The characteristic values of S_m are thus given by

$$(S_m)_f = - \frac{e\hbar}{2mc} \frac{m}{M_p} \gamma\overline{(H_z)}_{m=j} \frac{1}{2j}[f(f+1) - i(i+1) - j(j+1)]. \tag{2.7}$$

If we measure H in units $(e\hbar/2mc)/a^3$, and if $\Delta_m\nu_f$ is the distance of the level with quantum number f from the unperturbed level measured in cm^{-1}, then

$$\Delta_m \nu_f = -\frac{1}{2} R\alpha^2 \frac{m}{M_p} \gamma \, \overline{(H_z)}_{m=j} \frac{1}{2j} \left[f(f+1) - i(i+1) - j(j+1) \right] \tag{2.8}$$

where

$$R = \frac{1}{2} \alpha^2 mc/\hbar = 109{,}737$$

is the Rydberg constant, or

$$\Delta_m \nu_f = -\gamma \frac{\overline{(H_z)}_{m=j}}{j} \frac{1}{2} \left[f(j+1) - i(i+1) - j(j+1) \right] 1.585 \times 10^{-3} \, \text{cm}^{-1}.$$

In this formula the properties of the nucleus are characterized by the values of i and γ. The problem of magnetic hyperfine structure is now reduced to the problem of calculating $\overline{(H_z)}_{m=j}$, a quantity that depends only on the properties of the electrons and not on the structure of the nucleus.

3. Matrix elements of the magnetic interaction that are not diagonal with respect to the quantum numbers n and j

It may happen that two or more fine-structure levels are so near to each other that their distance is not large compared to the hyperfine structure. In that case we will also have to consider matrix elements of the perturbation operator that are not diagonal with respect to j and n. As long as we describe the states of electrons plus nucleus by the quantum numbers m_j, k—and the wave functions $\psi(n, j, m_j)_{\kappa k}$—these matrix elements are

$$-(n, j, m_j | H | n', j', m_j) (k | \mu | k').$$

If, however, we introduce the quantum numbers f and m_f, the $(n, j | n', j')$ part of the perturbation matrix is transformed into an expression of the form

$$(n, j, f | T | n', j', f) \, \delta(f - f') \, \delta(m'_f - m_f). \tag{3.1}$$

This follows from the fact that S_m commutes with F_x, F_y, F_z.

Now the following formulas hold (in each formula one is to take everywhere either the lower or the upper sign):

$$(n, j, m \mid H_x \pm iH_y \mid n', j + 1, m \mp 1)$$
$$= \pm (n, j \mid h \mid n', j + 1) \sqrt{(j \mp m + 1)(j \mp m + 2)},$$

$$(n, j, m \mid H_z \mid n', j + 1, m)$$
$$= (n, j \mid h \mid n', j + 1) \sqrt{(j + m + 1)(j - m + 1)},$$

$$(n, j, m \mid H_x \pm iH_y \mid n', j, m \mp 1)$$
$$= (n, j \mid h \mid n', j) \sqrt{(j \pm m)(j \mp m + 1)},$$

$$(n, j, m \mid H_z \mid n', j, m) = (n, j \mid h \mid n', j) m,$$

$$(n, j, m \mid H_x \pm iH_y \mid n', j - 1, m \mp 1) \qquad (3.2)$$
$$= \mp (n, j, \mid h \mid n', j - 1) \sqrt{(j \pm m)(j \pm m - 1)},$$

$$(n, j, m \mid H_z \mid n', j - 1, m) = (n, j \mid h \mid n', j - 1) \sqrt{(j - m)(j + m)};$$

all other matrix elements are zero.

The quantities $(n, j \mid h \mid n', j')$ can be determined by calculating one matrix element of one component of **H** for every possible combination $(n, j \mid n', j')$; for instance

$$(n, j \mid h \mid n', j + 1) = \frac{1}{\sqrt{2j + 1}} (n, j, j \mid H_z \mid n', j + 1, j),$$

$$(n, j \mid h \mid n', j) = \frac{1}{j} (n, j, j \mid H_z \mid n', j, j), \qquad (3.3)$$

$$(n, j \mid h \mid n', j - 1) = \frac{1}{\sqrt{2j - 1}} (n, j, j - 1 \mid H_z \mid n', j - 1, j - 1).$$

Now T can also be expressed in terms of these quantities. One obtains (*11*):

$$(n, j, f \mid T \mid n', j + 1, f) = -\gamma \frac{e\hbar}{2mc} \frac{m}{M_p} (n, j \mid h \mid n', j + 1)$$
$$\times \frac{1}{2} \sqrt{(f + j - i + 1)(f - j + i)(f + j + i + 2)(j + i + 1 - f)},$$

$$(n,j,f \,|\, T \,|\, n',j,f) = - \gamma \frac{e\hbar}{2mc} \frac{m}{M_p} (n,j \,|\, h \,|\, n',j)$$

$$\times \frac{1}{2} [f(f+1) - i(i+1) - j(j+1)],$$

$$(n,j,f \,|\, T \,|\, n',j-1,f) = - \gamma \frac{e\hbar}{2mc} \frac{m}{M_p} (n,j \,|\, h \,|\, n',j-1)$$

$$\times \frac{1}{2} \sqrt{(f+j+i+1)(j+i-f)(f+j-i)(f-j+i+1)}. \quad (3.4)$$

In actual applications the matrix elements will of course be expressed in cm^{-1}, and $(e\hbar/2mc)/a^3$ will be chosen as the unit of magnetic field strength.

4. Electrostatic interaction between nucleus and electrons

In this section we shall examine the $(n,j \,|\, n,j)$ matrix elements of the electrostatic interaction or, more accurately, of the difference between the true electrostatic interaction and the interaction between the electrons and a point charge. The $(n,j,m,k \,|\, n,j,m',k')$ matrix element of this difference is given by

$$(n,j,m,k \,|\, S_e \,|\, n,j,m',k') \;\; = - e^2 \int_{(6)} (n,j,m \,|\, \rho_e(\mathbf{r}_e) \,|\, n,j,m')$$

$$\times (k \,|\, \rho_k(\mathbf{r}_k) \,|\, k') \frac{1}{|\mathbf{r}_k - \mathbf{r}_e|} d\tau_k \, d\tau_e + e^2 Z \delta(k - k')$$

$$\times \int_{(3)} (n,j,m \,|\, \rho_e(\mathbf{r}_e) \,|\, n,j,m') \frac{1}{r_e} d\tau_e. \quad (4.1)$$

Here $-e\rho_e(\mathbf{r}_e)$ is the charge density of the electrons (ρ_e is the probability density), and $e\rho_k(\mathbf{r}_k)$ is the charge density of the nucleus. Let R be the radius of the nucleus, or more accurately, let $\rho_k(\mathbf{r}_k)$ be negligible for $r_k > R$. We shall first consider that part of the total region of integration for which $r_e > R$. We can then expand $1/|\mathbf{r}_k - \mathbf{r}_e|$ in a series:

$$\frac{1}{|\mathbf{r}_k - \mathbf{r}_e|} = \frac{1}{r_e} + \frac{r_k}{r_e^2} P_1(\cos \Theta) + \frac{r_k^2}{r_e^3} P_2(\cos \Theta) + \cdots,$$

where Θ is the angle between the directions of $\mathbf{r}_k$ and $\mathbf{r}_e$. Further,

$$r_k \, P_1 (\cos \Theta) = \frac{1}{r_e} \, (\mathbf{r}_k \cdot \mathbf{r}_e),$$

$$P_2(\cos \Theta) = \sum_{s=-2}^{s=2} P_2^s \vartheta(_e, \varphi_e) \, P_2^{-s} (\vartheta_k, \varphi_k),$$

where ϑ_e, φ_e, and ϑ_k, φ_k are the polar coordinates of $\mathbf{r}_e$ and $\mathbf{r}_k$, respectively; the spherical harmonics P_2^s will be chosen as follows:

$$P_2^{\pm 2} = \frac{3}{2\sqrt{6}} \, (x \pm iy)^2/r^2,$$

$$P_2^{\pm 1} = \frac{3}{\sqrt{6}} \, z \, (x \pm iy)/r^2,$$

$$P_2^0 = \left(\frac{3}{2} z^2 - \frac{1}{2} r^2 \right) r^{-2} = \left(z^2 - \frac{1}{2} x^2 - \frac{1}{2} y^2 \right) r^{-2}.$$

The integral from $r_e = R$ to $r_e = \infty$ reduces to (we omit temporarily the indices of ρ_e):

$$- e^2 \int_{\tau e > R} \rho_e(\mathbf{r}_e) \, \frac{1}{r_e} \, d\tau_e \int (k \, | \, \rho_k \, | \, k') \, d\tau_k \qquad (a)$$

$$+ Z e^2 \int_{\tau e > R} \rho_e(\mathbf{r}_e) \, \frac{1}{r_e} \, d\tau_e \, \delta \, (k - k') \qquad (b)$$

$$- e^2 \left[\int_{\tau e > R} \rho_e(\mathbf{r}_e) \, \frac{1}{r_e^3} \, \mathbf{r}_e \, d\tau_e \cdot \int (k \, | \, \rho_k \, | \, k') \, \mathbf{r}_k \, d\tau_k \right] \qquad (c)$$

$$- e^2 \sum_{s=-2}^{s=2} \int_{\tau e > R} \rho_e(\mathbf{r}_e) \, \frac{1}{r_e^3} \, P_2^s(\vartheta_e, \varphi_e) \, d\tau \int (k \, | \, \rho_k \, | \, k') \, r_k^2 \, P_2^{-s}(\vartheta_k, \varphi_k) \, d\tau_k. \quad (d)$$

The first two terms cancel, since

$$\int (k \, | \, \rho_k \, | \, k') \, d\tau_k = Z \delta \, (k - k').$$

The third term is zero, for ρ_k is invariant under an inversion with respect to the origin (a change of sign of all rectangular coordinates), whereas $\mathbf{r}_k$ changes its sign; thus only (d) remains. In this term it is permissible to integrate from $r_e = 0$, if the integration over the angles ϑ and φ is carried out before the integration over r_e. For if the electronic wave functions are written as a sum of products of single-electron wave functions, it is easily seen that those terms in ρ_e which do not vanish for $r_e = 0$ have spherical symmetry; but if these terms are multiplied by $P_2^s(\vartheta_e, \varphi_e)$ and are integrated over ϑ_e, φ_e, then the result is zero. These spherically symmetrical terms are the only terms that give an appreciable contribution to the integral from $r_e = 0$ to $r_e = R$. They give rise to a displacement of the energy levels that does not depend on f and which will be discussed more accurately in the next section.

We shall now deduce a simple expression for the characteristic values of (d). According to a general theorem, which can be proved by group-theoretical methods, one has:

$$\int (m|\rho_e|m') \frac{1}{r_e^3} P_2^s \, d\tau_e = (n,j|C_e|n,j)(m|\Pi_2^s(\mathbf{J})|m'), \quad (4.2)$$

where $\Pi_2^s(\mathbf{J})$ is a symmetrical harmonic polynomial, which is constructed from the components J_x, J_y, J_z in the same way as $r^2 P_2^s$ is constructed from x, y, z, or explicitly:

$$\Pi_2^{\pm 2} = \frac{3}{2\sqrt{6}} (J_x \pm iJ_y)^2,$$

$$\Pi_2^{\pm 1} = \frac{3}{2\sqrt{6}} \left[J_z (J_x \pm iJ_y) + (J_x \pm iJ_y) J_z \right],$$

$$\Pi_2^0 = \left(\frac{3}{2} J_z^2 - \frac{1}{2} J_x^2 - \frac{1}{2} J_y^2 - \frac{1}{2} J_z^2 \right).$$

We will write down only the matrix elements of Π_2^0:

$$(m|\Pi_2^0|m') = \left[\frac{3}{2} m^2 - \frac{1}{2} j(j+1) \right] \delta(m-m'). \quad (4.3)$$

The quantity C_e can be determined by calculating the left-hand side of (4.2) for $m = m' = j$ and $s = 0$:

$$(n,j|C_e|n,j) \left[\frac{3}{2} j^2 - \frac{1}{2} j(j+1) \right]$$

$$= \int (n,j,m=j|\rho_e|n,j,m=j) \frac{1}{r_e^3} P_2^0 \, d\tau_e$$

whence

$$(n,j|C_e|n,j) = \frac{1}{j(2j-1)} \int (n,j,j|\rho_e|n,j,j)$$

$$\times \frac{1}{r_e^3} (3\cos^3 \vartheta - 1) \, d\tau_e. \quad (4.4)$$

In the same way,

$$\int (k|\rho_k|k')\, r_k^2\, P_2^s\, d\tau_k = C_k\, (k|\Pi_2^s(\mathbf{I})|k'),\qquad(4.5)$$

with

$$C_k = \frac{1}{i(2i-1)}\int (i|\rho_k|i)\,(3z^2 - r^2)\, d\tau_k.\qquad(4.6)$$

The interaction matrix reduces to

$$-e^2\, C_e C_k \sum_{s=-2}^{s=+2} \Pi_2^s(\mathbf{J})\, \Pi_2^{-s}(\mathbf{I}).\qquad(4.7)$$

When F^2 is transformed to diagonal form the sum in (4.7) is also transformed to diagonal form. The characteristic values of this expression have been calculated by Kramers (26) by means of a method that is also applicable to higher harmonics. According to his result the characteristic values are given by

$$\frac{3}{8}\, K(K+1) - \frac{1}{2}\, i\,(i+1)\, j\,(j+1),\qquad(4.8)$$

where

$$K = f(f+1) - i(i+1) - j(j+1).$$

This result can also be derived in the following more elementary way. We must calculate:

$$A = \left(J_z^2 - \frac{1}{2}J_x^2 - \frac{1}{2}J_y^2\right)\left(I_z^2 - \frac{1}{2}I_x^2 - \frac{1}{2}I_y^2\right)$$

$$+ \left(\frac{3}{2\sqrt{6}}\right)^2 \Big[J_z(J_x+iJ_y)+(J_x+iJ_y)J_z\Big]\Big[I_z(I_x-iI_y)+(I_x-iI_y)I_z\Big]$$

$$+ \left(\frac{3}{2\sqrt{6}}\right)^2 \Big[J_z(J_x-iJ_y)+(J_x-iJ_y)J_z\Big]\Big[I_z(I_x+iI_y)+(I_x+iI_y)I_z\Big]$$

$$+ \left(\frac{3}{2\sqrt{6}}\right)^2 (J_x+iJ_y)^2\,(I_x-iI_y)^2$$

$$+ \left(\frac{3}{2\sqrt{6}}\right)^2 (J_x-iJ_y)^2\,(I_x+iI_y)^2.$$

If J_x, J_y, J_z and also I_x, I_y, I_z were commutable, then this expression would be equal to

$$B = \frac{3}{2} (J_x I_x + J_y I_y + J_z I_z)^2 - \frac{1}{2} (J_x^2 + J_y^2 + J_z^2)(I_x^2 + I_y^2 + I_z^2).$$

The difference between A and B is that in A there appears a term

$$a = \frac{3}{4} (J_x J_z + J_z J_x)(I_x I_z + I_z I_x)$$

instead of a term

$$b = \frac{3}{2} (J_x J_z I_x I_z + J_z J_x I_z I_x),$$

which occurs in B (and analogously for the combinations xy and yz). The difference can easily be calculated by means of the commutation relations; one finds

$$a - b = \frac{3}{4} J_y I_y,$$

and hence

$$A = B + \frac{3}{4} (J_x I_x + J_y I_y + J_z I_z) = \frac{3}{8} \cdot 2 (\mathbf{J} \cdot \mathbf{I}) [2(\mathbf{I} \cdot \mathbf{J}) + 1)] - \frac{1}{2} J^2 I^2,$$

which leads immediately to Kramers' result.

It is of some importance to notice that the center of gravity of the term n, j is not displaced by an interaction of this type; that is,

$$\sum_f (2f + 1) (\Delta_f \nu)_{\text{el}} = 0. \qquad (4.9)$$

To prove this, we remark that the left-hand side of (4.9) is the diagonal sum of the $(2i + 1)(2j + 1)$-dimensional perturbation matrix and therefore equal to (we write Tr for the diagonal sum):

$$- \text{Tr} \left[e^2 C_e C_k \sum_{s=-2}^{s=2} \Pi_2^s (\mathbf{J}) \, \Pi^{2-s} (\mathbf{I}) \right]$$

$$= - e^2 C_e C_k \sum_{s=-2}^{s=2} \text{Tr} \, [\Pi_2^s(\mathbf{J})] \cdot \text{Tr} \, [\Pi_2^{-s}(\mathbf{I})].$$

But

$$\text{Tr} \, [\Pi_2^s(\mathbf{J})] = \text{Tr} \, [\Pi_2^{-s}(\mathbf{I})] = 0.$$

For $s = 0$ this can easily be verified; by a simple group-theoretical argument one can infer that the result holds for all s.

Further, we remark that for $i = 0$ and $i = \frac{1}{2}$, $\Pi_2^s(\mathbf{I})$ is identically zero; this follows also from general theorems. In the same way, $\Pi_2^s(\mathbf{J}) = 0$ for $j = 0$ and $j = \frac{1}{2}$.

If we measure the energies in cm^{-1}, the radius r_e in units a, and the length r_k in 10^{-12} cm, the separation caused by the electrostatic interaction is given by

$$(\Delta_f \nu)_{\text{el}} = - \left\{ \frac{3 \cos^2 \vartheta_e - 1}{r_e^3} \right\}_{j,j} Q \frac{1}{(2i-1)(2j-1)ij} \left[\frac{3}{8} K(K+1) \right.$$
$$\left. - \frac{1}{2} ij(i+1)(j+1) \right] \times 7.9 \times 10^{-3} \text{ cm}^{-1}. \qquad (4.10)$$

The quantity in $\{\ \}$ is the mean value for the state $m_j = j$ (that is, the $(n,j,j \mid n,j,j)$ matrix element), and Q is given by

$$Q = \overline{(3z_k^2 - r_k^2)}_{i,\,i,}$$

measured in 10^{-24} cm^2. The total expression can be interpreted as the interaction between the electrons and an electric quadrupole.

Perhaps it would be more rational to use the quantity e^2/mc^2 (the classical radius of the electron) as a unit of length for the nucleus. Then the factor 7.9×10^{-3} must be replaced by $2R\alpha^4 = 0.62 \times 10^{-3}$.

5. *Interaction with the spherical terms in the charge distribution*

We shall now discuss the influence of the interior part of the perturbation integral on the energy levels; it is given by

$$I_e = - e^2 \int_{r_e < R} \int \rho_e(\mathbf{r}_e) \, \rho_k(\mathbf{r}_k) \frac{1}{|\mathbf{r}_e - \mathbf{r}_k|} d\tau_k \, d\tau_e$$
$$+ Ze^2 \int_{r_e < R} \rho_e(\mathbf{r}_e) \frac{1}{r_e} d\tau_e. \qquad (5.1)$$

We have already called attention to the fact that those terms in ρ_e which do not vanish for $r_e = 0$ have spherical symmetry. It follows that for small values of r_e the matrix ρ_e will be of the form

$$(n, j, m \,|\, \rho_e \,|\, n, j, m') = \delta\,(m - m')\,(n, j \,|\, \rho_e^0 \,|\, n, j\,),$$

and thence I_e is of the form

$$(m, k \,|\, I_e \,|\, m', k') = \delta\,(m - m')\,\delta\,(k - k')I_e^0.$$

In calculating I_e^0, however, we meet with an interesting difficulty. For states with spherical charge distribution (s and $p_{1/2}$ states) the solutions of Dirac's wave equation for the motion of an electron in the field of a point charge become infinite at $r = 0$. We can write

$$(n, j \,|\, \rho_e^0 \,|\, n, j\,) = (n, j \,|\, \rho_e^1 \,|\, n, j\,)\, r^{-\beta}, \tag{5.2}$$

with

$$\beta = 2 - 2\,\sqrt{1 - Z^2\alpha^2},$$

where ρ_e^1 does not depend on r. Using this expression we can calculate I_e^0. The result is

$$I_e^0 = + e^2\, \rho_e^1\, \frac{4\pi}{(3 - \beta)(2 - \beta)}\, \int (k \,|\, \rho_k \,|\, k)\, r^{2-\beta}\, d\tau_k. \tag{5.3}$$

The infinity of ρ_e at the origin, however, is a consequence of the assumption of a point nucleus; the exact wave functions corresponding to a continuous distribution of nuclear charge will remain finite at $r_e = 0$. If these exact wave functions were used, the value of I_e would also be modified. From a formal point of view this modification would correspond to a higher approximation of the perturbation theory, but in our case it seems rather doubtful whether the second-order terms will really be small. In order to estimate the order of magnitude of these second-order terms we will also calculate I_e on the assumption (assumption B) that the charge density is correctly represented by (5.2) outside the nucleus, but is constant inside the nucleus. The charge density inside the nucleus is then equal to

$$\rho_e^1\, R^{-\beta},$$

which leads to

$$I_e^0 = + e^2 \rho_e^1 \frac{2\pi}{3} R^{-\beta} \int (k | \rho_k | k) \, r^2 \, d\tau_k. \qquad (5.4)$$

Let us suppose that the nuclear charge is homogeneously distributed over the volume of a sphere with radius R (according to the theory of Heisenberg and Majorana this would approximately be the case). Then we find in first approximation

$$(I_e)_A = + Ze^2 \rho_e^1 R^{2-\beta} \frac{12\pi}{(5 - \beta)(3 - \beta)(2 - \beta)},$$

and on assumption B

$$(I_e)_B = + Ze^2 \rho_e^1 R^{2-\beta} \frac{2\pi}{5}.$$

For heavy nuclei the difference between these expressions is by no means negligible. For $\beta = 0.4$ ($Z = 82$), $(I_e^0)_B = 0.64 \, (I_e^0)_A$.

Of course it is always possible to use an expression of the form

$$I_e^0 = + Ze^2 \rho_e^1 \frac{2\pi}{5} R_e^{2-\beta},$$

but for heavy nuclei a rigorous determination of the "effective" radius R_e in terms of the distribution of nuclear charge would be possible only by means of much more elaborate calculations than we have given here.

The perturbation calculated in this section does not depend on the value of f; as long as only one isotope is considered it leads to a displacement and not to a separation of energy levels. The effective nuclear radii of the various isotopes of one element will, however, be slightly different, and thus the centers of gravity of the hyperfine structures belonging to different isotopes will be displaced relative to one another.

6. Discussion of the assumptions underlying our formulas

Before proceeding to actual applications of our formulas, we will try to analyse the assumptions underlying our calculations. With respect to the electrons in the atom, no assumptions have been made other than that the laws of quantum mechanics are valid and that the separations of the fine-structure levels are so large that we can confine ourselves to the first approximation of perturbation theory. Moreover, from Sections 3 and 8, we can see that this last assumption is not essential.

Further we have assumed that certain general results of quantum mechanics can be applied to the nucleus, and that the action of the nucleus on the electrons can be described as the action of current and charge distributions. It is important to emphasize that this is not equivalent to assuming that the nucleus can be described by the same wave equations as the atomic electrons. Even if it should prove impossible to define a current density and a charge density inside the nucleus, one would still expect that it should be possible to describe the external action of the nucleus in terms of an electric charge, a magnetic dipole, an electric quadrupole,..., connected with the angular momentum according to the general rules of group theory. The case is different, however, for that part of the interaction which takes place inside the nucleus.

The results of Section 5 are not very certain because of the (mathematical) difficulties involved in their derivation. But the foundations of these calculations also give rise to some doubts. It seems quite possible that the displacements caused by the interaction of the nucleus and the spherical part of the electronic charge density cannot be expressed in terms of the nuclear charge distribution, but that they depend on other properties of the nucleus. In the same way the possibility cannot be excluded that, in addition to the magnetic interaction between the nucleus and an s-electron (which itself is not completely determined by the magnetic moment of the nucleus), there exists another type of interaction that is proportional to $(\mathbf{I} \cdot \mathbf{J})$. It is difficult to say a priori whether or not the relative magnitude of this effect will be of the same order as the quantity $\delta H_0 / H_0$ introduced in Section 2.

7. Hyperfine structure and magnetic interaction

Let us assume that, starting from measurements on hyperfine structure of spectral lines, one has succeeded in deducing the position of the energy levels, in determining which levels belong to one and the same isotope, and in assigning f-values to these levels. Furthermore the values of i for the various isotopes will then be known. Hence we know the energies

$$E(n,j,f)_M,$$

where M denotes the mass number, or better, the differences of the energies belonging to a state n, j.

We shall first confine ourselves to the levels belonging to one isotope. It has been found that in general they follow rather accurately the interval rule; that is, the energies are given by a formula (we write ν for the energy expressed in cm^{-1}):

$$\nu(n,j,f) = \nu(n,j)^0 + \frac{A}{2}[f(f+1) - i(i+1) - j(j+1)], \quad (7.1)$$

where $\nu(n,j)^0$ is the center of gravity, and hence

$$\nu(n,j,i+j) - \nu(n,j;i+j-1) = A(i+j),$$
$$\nu(n,j,i+j-1) - \nu(n,j;i+j-2) = A(i+j-1),$$

and so on.

The question must now be examined whether or not the separations can be ascribed to a nuclear moment and whether the magnitude of this moment can be determined. In order to do this one has to know the quantity $\overline{(H_z)}_{j,\,j}$, the mean value of the z-component of the magnetic field at the nucleus produced by the electrons in the state $m = j$. The calculation of this quantity is comparatively easy for an atom with one electron outside a closed shell. We shall return later on to the formulas applying to that case and to the foundations of their derivation. The problem is far more difficult for an atom having more than one valence electron. To a first approximation the wave function for a particular state of these electrons can be written as a sum of products of wave functions for the separate electrons, only such wave functions being used as correspond to one definite configuration (that is, one set of values n_i, l_i).

Detailed calculations of $\overline{(H_z)}_{j,\,j}$ for such cases have been carried out by Breit and Wills (6), whereas at an earlier date Goudsmit (21) already worked out a method, based on the application of sum rules, that made it possible to calculate the separations caused by the electrons separately from the splittings of the different terms belonging to one configuration.

It has been found, however, that the approximation to the wave functions by "functions of a given configuration" is not always permissible. In general, every configuration will be more or less perturbed; the configurations will thus get mixed up. If a given configuration is perturbed by another configuration with large hyperfine structure, the influence of the perturbation on the hyperfine structure will be considerable, even when the perturbation is small. Fermi and Segré (16) have called attention to this circumstance.

The result of the most recent examinations is that there is no reason to doubt the essential correctness of the assumption that the separations are due to the interaction of the electrons with a magnetic dipole. In those cases in which reliable calculations are possible, there is a satisfactory agreement between the values of the magnetic moment calculated from the separations of different terms.

One must not forget, however, that the accuracy with which the calculations can be carried out is not very high; with the one exception of Li II the errors may easily amount to 10%. Thus the possibility remains that corrections of this order of magnitude must be applied to (2.8) even in cases where the interval rule strictly holds.

8. Deviations from the interval rule

More accurate measurements show that the hyperfine structure levels do not always follow the interval rule. These deviations have two different causes. In the first place, they can be a consequence of electric interaction with the nucleus; in the second place they can be due to a second-order effect in the magnetic interaction. Such a second-order effect is to be expected whenever the distance of two fine-structure levels is not large compared to the hyperfine structure separations.

For simplicity we will first consider the case in which only two fine-structure levels (n, j) and (n', j') lie close together. Let D be their separation. Then by the magnetic interaction with the nucleus both levels are separated into a number of components. An f-value may occur twice: once for a level belonging to the first fine-structure level, and once for a level belonging to the second one. The two levels with the same f-value will now perturb each other, and in order to find the true energy levels one has to determine the roots of a two-rowed secular equation. This equation will be given by (the energy is measured in cm^{-1}):

$$\begin{vmatrix} \epsilon - \nu(n',j')^0 - \dfrac{1}{2}A(n',j')\,B(j') & (n'\,j'f\,|\,T\,|\,njf) \\[2ex] (n,j,f\,|\,T\,|\,n',j',j) & \epsilon - \nu(n,j)^0 - \dfrac{1}{2}\,A(n,j)\,B(j) \end{vmatrix} = 0$$

$$(8.1)$$

where

$$B(j) = f(f+1) - i(i+1) - j(j+1)$$

The matrix elements of T are given in Section 3. We repeat the formulas introducing the units mentioned at the end of Section 3:

$$(n,j,f\,|\,T\,|\,n',j+1,f) = -\,\gamma\,\frac{(n,j,j\,|\,H_z\,|\,n',j+1,j)}{\sqrt{2j+1}}$$

$$\times \frac{1}{2}\sqrt{(f+j+i+2)(f+j-i+1)(j+i+1-f)(f-j+i)}$$
$$\times 1.585 \times 10^{-3}\ \text{cm}^{-1},$$

$$(n,j,f\,|\,T\,|\,n',j,f) = -\,\gamma\,\frac{(n,j,j\,|\,H_z\,|\,n',j,j)}{j}$$

$$\times \frac{1}{2}[f(f+1) - i(i+1) - j(j+1)] \times 1.585 \times 10^{-3}\,\text{cm}^{-1}, \quad (8.2)$$

$$(n,j,f\,|\,T\,|\,n',j-1,f) = -\,\gamma\,\frac{(n,j,j-1\,|\,H_z\,|\,n',j-1,j-1)}{\sqrt{2j-1}}$$

$$\times \frac{1}{2}\sqrt{(f+j-i)(f-j+i+1)(f+j+i+1)(j+i-f)}$$
$$\times 1.585 \times 10^{-3}\,\text{cm}^{-1}.$$

Further, we have

$$A(n',j') = -\,\gamma\,\frac{(n',j',j\,|\,H_z\,|\,n',j',j)}{j} \times 1.585 \times 10^{-3}\ \text{cm}^{-1},$$

$$(8.3)$$

$$A(n,j) = -\,\gamma\,\frac{(n,j,j\,|\,H_z\,|\,n,j,j)}{j} \times 1.585 \times 10^{-3}\ \text{cm}^{-1}.$$

In the same way we can write down the secular determinant for the case in which more than two n, j levels lie close together.

In most cases the influence of the higher-order corrections will be small compared to the total hyperfine structure. An approximate solution of the secular equation is then sufficient. The result is as follows. By setting

$$\nu_1(n,j,f) = \nu(n,j)^0 + \frac{1}{2} A(n,j) [f(f+1) - i(i+1) - j(j+1)],$$
$$(8.4)$$

$$\nu_1(n',j',f) = \nu(n',j')^0 + \frac{1}{2} A(n',j')[f(f+1) - i(i+1) - j'(j'+1)],$$

and letting $\nu(n', j', f)$ and $\nu(n, j, f)$ be the respective energy values, we then obtain

$$\nu(n',j',f) = \nu_1(n',j',f) + \delta\nu,$$
$$\nu(n,j,f) = \nu_1(n,j,f) - \delta\nu,$$
$$(8.5)$$

with

$$\delta\nu = \frac{|(n,j;f|T|n',j';f)|^2}{\nu_1(n',j';f) - \nu_1(n,j;f)}.$$
$$(8.6)$$

One may replace ν_1 in the denominator by ν; in most cases one can even write

$$\delta\nu = \frac{|(n,j,f|T|n',j',f)|^2}{\nu(n',j')^0 - \nu(n,j)^0} = \frac{|(n,j,f|T|n',j',f)|^2}{D}.$$
$$(8.7)$$

The perturbation results in a symmetric repulsion of the two terms.

The rigorous formulas are as follows. If we write the secular equation in the form

$$\begin{vmatrix} \epsilon - \nu_1 & T \\ T & \epsilon - \nu_1' \end{vmatrix} = 0,$$

then the roots are given by

$$\epsilon = \frac{\nu_1 + \nu_1'}{2} \pm \frac{\nu_1 - \nu_1'}{2} \left[\sqrt{1 + \frac{4T^2}{(\nu_1 - \nu_1')^2}} \right].$$
$$(8.8)$$

The rigorous result is again symmetrical repulsion of the two levels; we also see that in (8.6) only quantities of the order T^4/D^3 have been neglected. When more than two levels perturb each other, the influence of these perturbations can in first approximation be described as a mutual repulsion in each pair of two levels.

In order for us to picture the influence of the higher-order perturbations without further calculation, we can state the following rules:

(1) Levels with equal f repel one another.
(2) The order of magnitude of the repulsion is given by (hyperfine structure splitting)^2/(separation of nonperturbed levels), since T is of the same order as A.
(3) Only levels with $j' - j = 0$ or ± 1 perturb one another.
(4) The ratios of the repulsions of pairs of levels with the same n, j and n', j' but different f can be deduced from (8.2) and (8.3).

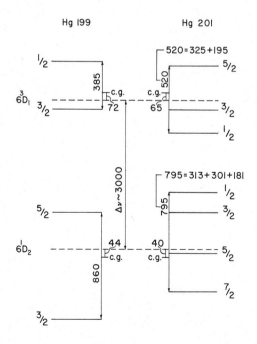

Figure 1

These rules do not depend on special assumptions concerning the wave functions of the states n, j and n', j'. Only if we want to calculate the quantity $(n, j, j \,|\, H_z \,|\, n', j', j)$ must approximate expressions for the wave functions be introduced.

As an example we discuss the perturbations in the hyperfine structure of the 6^3D_1 and 6^1D_2 terms of Hg. For the isotopes Hg_{199} and Hg_{201} the i-values are $1/2$ and $3/2$ respectively. The ratio of the magnetic moments is $0.9/1$, that of the γ-factors,

$$\gamma_{199}/\gamma_{201} = 2.7/1.$$

Schüler and Jones (34) have observed the levels shown in Figure 1 (the distances are given in 10^{-3} cm^{-1}). For the term 6^1D_2 of Hg_{201} the interval rule does not hold. Now the levels with equal f will repel one another. The order of magnitude of the repulsion is roughly $(400/3000) \times 400 \approx 50$, and this is of the same order of magnitude as the deviations from the interval rule. For Hg_{199} there is only one pair of terms with equal f; for Hg_{201} there are three (with $f = \frac{1}{2}, f = \frac{3}{2}, f = \frac{5}{2}$). For the ratio of the repulsions of these terms one finds:

$$\delta_{1/2} : \delta_{3/2} : \delta_{5/2} = 1 : 2.8 : 3.$$

The repulsion can be calculated in detail, if, as do Schüler and Jones, we admit the assumption that the centers of gravity of the unperturbed terms of the odd isotopes coincide with the terms of the even isotopes (these terms are indicated by the broken lines in Figure 1). For the repulsion of the levels with $f = \frac{3}{2}$ of Hg_{199} one finds $\delta_{3/2} = 108$, whence

$$\frac{1}{3500}\left[\gamma_{199}(6^3D_1; 1 \,|\, H_z \,|\, 6^1D_2; 1)\frac{1}{\sqrt{3}}\right.$$

$$\left.\times \frac{1}{2} \times 1.585 \times 10^{-3}\right]^2 \times 3 \times 5 \times 1 \times 1 = 108,$$

and

$$\left[\gamma_{201}(6^3D_1; 1 \,|\, H_z \,|\, 6^1D_2; 1)\frac{1}{\sqrt{3}}\right.$$

$$\left.\times \frac{1}{2} \times 1.585 \times 10^{-3}\right]^2 = \frac{3500 \times 108}{15 \times (2.7)^2} = 3460.$$

It then follows that

$$\delta_{1/2} = \frac{1}{2200} \times 3460 \times 1 \times 1 \times 5 \times 3 \approx 24,$$

$$\delta_{3/2} = \frac{1}{2500} \times 3460 \times 2 \times 2 \times 6 \times 2 \approx 66,$$

$$\delta_{5/2} = \frac{1}{3100} \times 3460 \times 3 \times 3 \times 7 \times 1 \approx 70.$$

If with these values we calculate the position of the unperturbed terms, the deviations from the interval rule are indeed appreciably reduced. The agreement with the interval rule, however, is not perfect, and the discrepancies are larger than the limits of error admitted by Schüler ($\pm 5 \times 10^{-3}$ cm^{-1}). The agreement cannot be improved by assuming a displacement of the center of gravity. One might at first be inclined to believe that the remaining deviations are caused by electrostatic interaction, but the way in which they depend on f seems to exclude that possibility. Schüler and Jones have shown that the interval rule is satisfied if

$$\delta_{1/2} = 42, \qquad \delta_{3/2} = 64, \qquad \delta_{5/2} = 78.$$

It seems to us that the question has not yet been completely cleared up. The most simple way of explaining the difficulty is to assume, along with Goudsmit and Bacher (*22*), that the remaining discrepancies are partly due to errors of measurement, and partly to perturbations by other terms.

As a second example we examine the perturbations in the hyperfine structure of the 6^3D_1 and 7^3D_1 terms of Indium. For Indium $i = 9/2$. The only term by which n^3D_1 can be perturbed is the term n^3D_2. The distance D is 34 cm^{-1} for 6^3D_1, and 18 cm^{-1} for 7^3D_1. The separations for $6D_1$ and $7D_1$ are almost equal; roughly, we have:

$$\nu(11/2) - \nu(9/2) \approx 950 \times 10^{-3} \text{ cm}^{-1},$$

$$\nu(9/2) - \nu(7/2) \approx 800 \times 10^{-3} \text{ cm}^{-1}.$$

In calculating the repulsion of levels with equal f, we will only take into account the interaction of the nucleus and the s-electron. This is permissible, since the virtual equality of the separations of $6D$ and $7D$ shows that the interaction of the nucleus with the

d-electron is small. (It must not be forgotten that the perturbations we want to calculate form only a small part of the total hyperfine structure.) Further, we assume Russell-Saunders coupling. The distance between the ^1D term and the ^3D terms is much larger than the mutual distances between the ^3D terms themselves; moreover, for the ^3D terms Landé's interval rule is accurately fulfilled. The wave functions of the ^3D terms can now be written as linear combinations of products of functions d_m of the coordinates of the d-electron $(-2 \leq m \leq 2)$ with functions $s_n(-1 \leq n \leq 1)$ of the coordinates of the s-electron and the spin of the s- and of the d-electron. The linear combinations corresponding to a $^3D_2$, $m = 1$ state and a $^3D_1$, $m = 1$ state can be written down directly by means of general formulas. In practical calculation, however, it is usually easier to construct the functions in the following way. We start from the function d_2s_1 corresponding to the state $^3D_3$, $m = 3$; if the operator $J_x - iJ_y = (d_x - id_y) + (s_x - is_y)$ (where d_x, d_y, d_z are the components of the orbital angular momentum, and where s_x, s_y, s_z are the components of the resultant spin) is applied to this function, there results a function proportional to the function $^3D_3$, $m = 2$. The function $^3D_2$, $m = 2$ is orthogonal to this function.

Applying the operator $J_x - iJ_y$ to the functions $^3D_3$, $m = 2$ and $^3D_2$, $m = 2$, we obtain the functions $^3D_3$, $m = 1$ and $^3D_2$, $m = 1$; the function $^3D_1$, $m = 1$ is orthogonal to these functions.

In this way we obtain the following scheme.

	$^3D_3$	$^3D_2$	$^3D_1$
$m = 3$	d_2s_1		
$m = 2$	$\dfrac{1}{\sqrt{6}}(2\,d_1s_1 + \sqrt{2}\,d_2s_0)$	$\dfrac{1}{\sqrt{6}}(\sqrt{2}\,d_1s_1 - 2d_2s_0)$	
$m = 1$	$\dfrac{1}{\sqrt{15}}(\sqrt{6}\,d_0s_1 + 2\sqrt{2}\,d_1s_0 + d_2s_{-1})$	$\dfrac{1}{\sqrt{6}}(\sqrt{3}\,d_0s_1 - d_1s_0 - \sqrt{2}\,d_2s_{-1})$	$\dfrac{1}{\sqrt{10}}(d_0s_1 - \sqrt{3}_1ds_0 + \sqrt{6}d_2s_{-1})$

$$(8.9)$$

In simple cases the construction of such a scheme takes less time than the application of general formulas.

We shall now calculate the matrix elements of H_z. Setting

$$(s_1 | H_z | s_1) = H_s,$$

we have

$$(s_1 | H_z | s_1) = H_s,$$
$$(s_0 | H_z | s_0) = 0,$$
$$(s_{-1} | H_z | s_{-1}) = - H_s,$$

and

$$({}^3D_1; 1 | H_z | {}^3D_1; 1) = - \frac{1}{2} H_s,$$

$$({}^3D_1; 1 | H_z | {}^3D_2; 1) = + \frac{3}{2\sqrt{5}} H_s,$$

$$({}^3D_2; 2 | H_z | {}^3D_2; 2) = + \frac{1}{3} H_s.$$

For the unperturbed separations of the $^3D_1$ terms we find

$$\Delta \nu_f = + \gamma \frac{1}{2} H_s \frac{1}{2} [f(f+1) - i(i+1) - j(j+1)]$$
$$\times 1.585 \times 10^{-3} \,\text{cm}^{-1}.$$

It is easily seen that H_s must be a negative quantity, the term with the largest f-value being the lowest one. The measured separation of 1760 units leads to

$$H_s \gamma \times 1.585 = -350.$$

With this value we can now roughly calculate the position of the hyperfine structure levels of $^3D_2$. The result is shown in Figure 2.

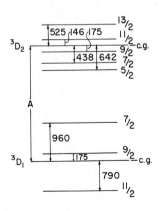

Figure 2

The object of this calculation is only to obtain a sufficient approximation for the distance between levels with equal f. If we let D be the distance between the centers of gravity, we then have:

for the distance $\quad 7/2 \rightarrow \quad 7/2$: $\qquad D - 1400$;

for the distance $\quad 9/2 \rightarrow \quad 9/2$: $\qquad D - \quad 350$;

for the distance $11/2 \rightarrow 11/2$: $\qquad D + \quad 940$.

Using these values we find, by applying (8.6),

$$10^{-6}\delta_{11/2} = 1.61/(D + 940),$$
$$10^{-6}\delta_{9/2} = 1.76/(D - 350),$$
$$10^{-6}\delta_{7/2} = 1.06/(D - 1400).$$

For 6^3D we have $D = 34{,}000$, and hence

$$\delta_{11/2} = 46.2, \qquad \delta_{9/2} = 52.3, \qquad \delta_{7/2} = 32.5.$$

The perturbation leads to a decrease of 6.1 units in the distance $\nu(11/2) - \nu(9/2)$, and to an increase of 19.8 units in the distance $\nu(9/2) - \nu(7/2)$.

According to Paschen (30) the separations are

$$\nu(11/2) - \nu(9/2) = 950.5$$

and

$$\nu(9/2) - \nu(7/2) = 798.3.$$

The unperturbed separations become

$$\nu(11/2) - \nu(9/2) = 956.6$$

and

$$\nu(9/2) - \nu(7/2) = 778.5 = (9/11) \times 956.6 - 4.$$

The deviation from the interval rule, which amounted to 20 units for the experimental separations, is thus reduced to 4 units.

This result is satisfactory, but for the $7D$ terms the result is less satisfactory. Here $D = 18$, hence

$$\delta_{11/2} = 85.0, \qquad \delta_{9/2} = 99.7, \qquad \delta_{7/2} = 63.8.$$

The measured separations are

$$\nu(11/2) - \nu(9/2) = 952.6$$
$$\nu(9/2) - \nu(7/2) = 811.5 = (9/11) \times 952.6 + 32.$$

The unperturbed distances become

$$\nu(11/2) - \nu(9/2) = 967.3$$

and

$$\nu(9/2) - \nu(7/2) = 775.6 = (9/11) \times 967.3 - 16.$$

In this case the calculated perturbation is too large. We have not succeeded in explaining the discrepancy. The fact that the deviations for 7^3D are larger than for 6^3D seems to exclude an explanation in terms of electrostatic interaction. It may be, however, that the assumption of Russell-Saunders coupling is not quite justified or that the terms are influenced by perturbations other than those considered in our calculation.

Perturbations of the type examined in this section were found for the first time by Schüler (*33*) in the Li II spectrum, and have been discussed theoretically by Pauli and Güttinger (*23*). The foregoing discussion of the perturbations in the Hg spectrum is almost identical with that given by Casimir (*9*). Later on the same problem was studied by Goudsmit and Bacher (*22*) by a different method. They also calculated the value of the constant, which is here derived from the experimentally determined position of the levels of Hg_{199}. Their assumptions about the state of coupling, however, are not quite justified, but their results are in agreement with those given here.

Although the application of Goudsmit's method to a special case is undoubtedly much simpler than the derivation of the general formulas used in this paper, we nevertheless believe that our method of treating the perturbations has considerable advantages in that they show how far the results obtained depend or do not depend on special assumptions concerning the wave functions.

9. Detailed discussion of the influence of an electric quadrupole moment

Deviations from the interval rule may also arise from the electrostatic interaction between the nucleus and the outer electrons. In Section 4 we derived the formula

$$(\Delta \nu_f)_{\text{el}} = - \left\{ \frac{\overline{3 \cos^2 \vartheta - 1}}{r^3} \right\}_{j, f}$$

$$\times Q \times \frac{\left[\frac{3}{8} K(K + 1) - \frac{1}{2} ij(i + 1)(j + 1) \right]}{ij(2i - 1)(2j - 1)} \times 7.9 \times 10^{-3} \, \text{cm}^{-1},$$

$$(9.1)$$

with

$$K = f(f + 1) - i(i + 1) - j(j + 1)$$

and

$$Q = \overline{(3z_k^2 - r_k^2)}_{i, \, i}.$$

The expression in $\{\}$ is an average over the charge density of the electrons (we have omitted the suffix e), the radius of the first hydrogen orbit being chosen as the unit of length; Q is an average over the charge density in the nucleus, the unit of length being 10^{-12}.

The mean value of $3 \cos^2 \vartheta - 1$ is a measure of the deviation from spherical symmetry of the charge density of the electrons; it is zero for a spherical distribution, positive for a prolate distribution, and negative for an oblate distribution. The expression in braces is thus positive or negative depending on whether the charge distribution of the electrons is prolate or oblate in the direction of angular momentum. According to Schüler and Schmidt (35) this may be illustrated by a schematic representation (Figure 3).

In the same way, Q is positive or negative depending on whether the nucleus is prolate or oblate in the direction of its angular momentum. The quantity Q will be called the electric quadrupole moment of the nucleus.

It is now easily seen that in the state in which j and i are parallel to each other the interaction energy is negative when both distributions are prolate or when both are oblate. The factor

$$\frac{\frac{3}{8} K(K + 1) - \frac{1}{2} ij(i + 1)(j + 1)}{(2i - 1)(2j - 1) ij}$$

is the quantum-mechanical analogue of the classical expression

$$\frac{1}{4} \left[\frac{3}{2} \cos^2(i, j) - \frac{1}{2} \right],$$

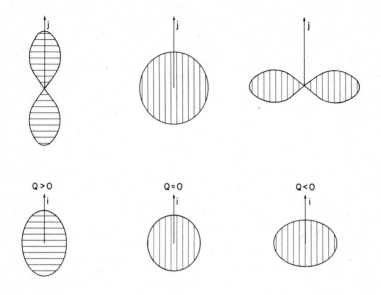

Figure 3

and reduces to this expression in the limit of high quantum numbers.

If for a definite term separations have been found that do not obey the interval rule, although there are no neighboring terms that can give rise to deviations of the right order of magnitude, then one should try a formula of the type

$$\nu_f - \nu_0 = \frac{A}{2} K + B \left[\frac{3}{8} K(K+1) - \frac{1}{2} ij(i+1)(j+1) \right]. \quad (9.2)$$

If for this term the number of hyperfine structure levels is larger than three, then the examination of the levels corresponding to only one fine-structure term will readily give a check on our assumption. If there are only three possible f-values, however, one can always represent the separations by a formula of the form (9.2). In general, a reliable determination of the quadrupole moment will be possible only in cases where deviations from the interval rule have been determined for several terms, for then the Q values derived from the separations of these terms can be compared with each other.

In order to derive Q from B in (9.2) one must know the quantity

$$C_e = \left(\frac{3 \cos^2 \vartheta - 1}{r^3} \right)_{j,\, j}.$$

We shall give approximate expressions for this quantity, confining ourselves to those cases in which only one electron contributes to C_e.

Let us consider one electron without spin and with orbital angular momentum l. The wave functions will be of the form

$$\psi_{n,\, l,\, m}(r, \vartheta, \varphi) = f_{n,\, l}(r) Y_l^m(\vartheta, \varphi),$$

whence

$$\left(\frac{3 \cos^2 \vartheta - 1}{r^3} \right)_{m,\, m} = \left(\frac{1}{r^3} \right)_{n,\, l} \overline{(3 \cos^2 \vartheta - 1)}_{m,\, m},$$

where the mean value $\overline{(1/r^3)}$ does not depend on m. A simple integration yields

$$\overline{(3 \cos^2 \vartheta - 1)}_{l,\, l} = - \frac{2l}{2l + 3}, \qquad (9.3)$$

and hence

$$\overline{(3 \cos^2 \vartheta - 1)}_{m,\, m} = - \frac{3m^2 - l(l + 1)}{(2l - 1)\, l}\, \frac{2l}{2l + 3}. \qquad (9.4)$$

The negative sign in (9.4) corresponds to the fact that in an orbital model the plane of the orbit is perpendicular to the angular momentum vector.

If an l-orbit is coupled to a spin vector S (the corresponding wave functions are denoted by S_m) then the wave function for the state j, $m_j = j$ will be given by an expression

$$\Psi_j = \sum_{m_l} A\,(l, S)_{j,\, m_l} f_{n,\, l}(r)\, Y_l^{m_l}\, S_{j - m_l}. \qquad (9.5)$$

It then follows that

$$\left(\frac{3 \cos^2 \vartheta - 1}{r^3} \right)_{j,\, j} = \left(\frac{1}{r^3} \right)_{n,\, l} \overline{(3 \cos^2 \vartheta - 1)}_{j,\, j},$$

and

$$\overline{(3 \cos^2 \vartheta - 1)}_{j,\, j}$$

$$= - \sum_{m_l} \left| A\,(l, S)_{j,\, m} \right|^2 \frac{3m_l^2 - l(l + 1)}{l(2l - 1)}\, \frac{2l}{2l + 3}. \qquad (9.6)$$

Using general formulas for $A_{j,\,m_l}$ we can now calculate the required average for any set of values of l, S, and j.

We shall give here only the values of $\left|A_{j,\,m_l}\right|^2$ for two cases of special importance.

(1) An orbital angular momentum l is coupled to a spin momentum 1; this case will occur in two-electron spectra. For the wave functions we find by means of the procedure explained in Section 8 the scheme given on p. 32.

It follows, then, that

$$^3L_{l+1}\left|A_{l+1,\,l}\right|^2 = 1,$$

$$^3L_l \quad \left|A_{l,\,l}\right|^2 = \frac{l}{l+1}, \qquad \left|A_{l,\,l-1}\right|^2 = \frac{1}{l+1},$$

$$^3L_l \quad \left|A_{l,\,l}\right|^2 = \frac{l}{l+1}, \qquad \left|A_{l,\,l-1}\right|^2 = \frac{1}{l+1},$$

$$\left|A_{l-1,\,l-2}\right|^2 = \frac{1}{l(2l+1)}.$$

(2) In the same way we find for a p-electron coupled with a spin S of arbitrary value the following scheme:

	$m_l = 1$	$m_l = 0$	$m_l = -1$
$j = S+1$	1		
$j = S$	$\dfrac{1}{S+1}$	$\dfrac{S}{S+1}$	
$j = S-1$	$\dfrac{1}{S(2S+1)}$	$\dfrac{2S-1}{S(2S+1)}$	$\dfrac{2S-1}{2S+1}$

In the case of two-electron configurations deviations from Russell-

m_j	$^3L_{l+1}$	^3L_l	$^3L_{l-1}$
$l+1\,s_l l_l$			
l	$-\dfrac{1}{\sqrt{2l+2}}\,(\sqrt{2s_0\,l_l}+\sqrt{2l}\,s_1\,l_{l-1})$	$-\dfrac{1}{\sqrt{2l+2}}\,(\sqrt{2l\,s_0\,l_l}-\sqrt{2}\,s_1\,l_{l-1})$	$\dfrac{1}{\sqrt{l(2l+1)}}\,(\sqrt{l(2l-1)}\,l_l\,s_{-1}$
$l-1$	$\dfrac{1}{4\sqrt{(l+1)(2l+1)}}\,(2s_{-1}\,l_l+4\sqrt{l}\,s_0\,l_{l-1}$ $+\,2\sqrt{l(2l-1)}\,s_1\,l_{l-2})$	$\dfrac{1}{2\sqrt{l(l+1)}}\,(2\sqrt{l}\,s_{-1}\,l_l+2(l-1)\,s_0\,l_{l-1}$ $-\,2\sqrt{2l-1}\,s_1\,l_{l-2})$	$-\sqrt{2l-1}\,l_{l-1}\,s_0+l_{l-2}\,s_1)$

Saunders coupling can easily be taken into account. The wave functions for the states $^3L_{l+1}$ and $^3L_{l-1}$ will not be changed; the wave functions for the ^3L_l and ^1L_l states will be of the form

$$^3\Psi_l = \alpha\,^3L_l + \beta\,^1L_l,$$

$$^1\Psi_l = -\beta\,^3L_l + \alpha\,^1L_l. \tag{9.7}$$

For ^3L_l it follows that

$$\overline{(3\cos^2\vartheta - 1)}_{l,\,l} = -\frac{2l}{2l+3}\left[\frac{l^2+l-3}{l(l+1)} + \beta^2\,\frac{3}{l(l+1)}\right], \tag{9.8}$$

and for ^1L_l, that

$$\overline{(3\cos^2\vartheta - 1)}_{l,\,l} = -\frac{2l}{2l+3}\left[1 - \frac{3\beta^2}{l(l+1)}\right]. \tag{9.9}$$

The value of β can be determined from the position of the fine structure terms in the following way (compare Section 11). Let d be the distance of the "singlet" and the "triplet" term, and let Δ the distance between the observed position of the triplet term and the position it should have according to the Landé rule. Then

$$\beta^2 = \frac{\Delta}{d}. \tag{9.10}$$

The most important application of our formula is to the case of P and D terms. The results for these terms are:

$\overline{(3\cos^2\vartheta - 1)}_{j,\,j}$		$\overline{(3\cos^2\vartheta - 1)}_{j,\,j}$	
$^3D_3$	$-\dfrac{4}{7}$	$^3P_2$	$-\dfrac{2}{5}$
$^3D_2$	$-\dfrac{2}{7}(1+\beta^2)$	$^3P_1$	$+\dfrac{1}{5}(1-3\beta^2)$
$^3D_1$	$-\dfrac{1}{5}$	$^3P_0$	0
$^1D_2$	$-\dfrac{4}{7}(1-\dfrac{1}{2}\beta^2)$	$^1P_1$	$-\dfrac{2}{5}(1-\dfrac{3}{2}\sin^2\vartheta)$

We also recall the well-known formula for the mean value of $1/r^3$ (expressed in units of $1/a^3$):

$$\overline{\left(\frac{1}{r^3}\right)} = \frac{Z_i Z_0^2}{n^{*3} l \, (l + \frac{1}{2}) \, (l + 1)}. \qquad (9.11)$$

Here Z_i, the nuclear charge number for the "interior part" of the orbit, is equal to the total nuclear charge number diminished by a screening correction; Z_0 is the exterior charge number (for neutral atoms $Z_0 = 1$); and n^* is the effective quantum number.

On the other hand, the doublet separation (in cm^{-1}) is given by the nonrelativistic formula

$$\delta = (2l + 1) Z_i \overline{\left(\frac{1}{r^3}\right)} \times 2.911 \text{ cm}^{-1}, \qquad (9.12)$$

whence

$$\overline{\left(\frac{1}{r^3}\right)} = \frac{\delta_L / 2.911}{(2l + 1) Z_i}.$$

We shall return later on to the derivation of these formulas.

10. The hyperfine structure of europium and cassiopeium*

Deviations from the interval rule of the type described in the preceding section were found for the first time by Schüler and Schmidt (35) in the hyperfine structure of europium. There are two isotopes, Eu_{151} and Eu_{153}; for both isotopes $i = 5/2$. The value of the magnetic moment of Eu_{151} is roughly twice the value of the magnetic moment of Eu_{153}. The deviations from the interval rule for the heavy isotope, however, are about twice as large as those for the light isotope. From this fact it follows with certainty that the deviations from the interval rule cannot be caused by second-order perturbation, since in that case the perturbations for the light isotope should be four times as large as the perturbations for the heavy one. It was shown by the author that the deviations are in quantitative agreement with the assumption that they are due to electric interaction with the nucleus. For the quadrupole moments the following values were found:

$$Eu_{151} \qquad (3z^2 - r^2)_{i, \, i} = + 1.5 \times 10^{-24},$$
$$Eu_{153} \qquad (3z^2 - r^2)_{i, \, i} = + 3.2 \times 10^{-24}.$$

As to the reliability of these results, we believe that they establish

* Throughout this paper the name cassiopeium and the symbol Cp are used for the element of atomic number 7, commonly known in the United States as lutetium (Lu).

beyond doubt the existence of an electric quadrupole moment. Three terms were investigated (namely, $^{10}P_{9/2}$, $^{10}P_{7/2}$, $^{8}P_{7/2}$; the discussion can be carried out by means of the formulas of Section 9), and the agreement between theory and experiment is such that a fortuitous coincidence seems excluded. Furthermore, the value $3.2/1.5 = 2.1$ for the ratio of the quadrupole moments follows unambiguously from the experiments. The absolute value of these moments, however, is less certain, since it is very difficult to estimate the accuracy of the value of $(1/r^3)$ calculated by means of (*9.11*). The value of n^* was estimated by Russell and King (*32*); but the spectrum is not sufficiently well known for an accurate determination of the series limit to be possible. Still we do not believe that the values of the quadrupole moment will be in error by more than 25%.

The second element concerning which data were published by Schüler and Schmidt (*36*) is cassiopeium (lutetium), ($Z = 71$, $M = 175$). The spectrum of singly ionized Cp is a two-electron spectrum. The hyperfine structure was investigated for the terms $^{3}D_3$, $^{3}D_2$, $^{3}D_1$ and $^{3}P_2$, $^{3}P_1$. The value of i was found to be $7/2$ (in determining this value Schüler and Schmidt made use of the intensity rules). The hyperfine structure of all these terms shows deviations from the interval rule far outside the limits of accuracy of the measurements (they amount to as much as 70 units!).

Schüler and Schmidt showed that the hyperfine structure can be represented with a high degree of accuracy (1 or 2 units) by formulas of the type

$$\nu_f - \nu_0 = a_1 \frac{K}{2ij} + a_2 \left(\frac{K}{2ij} \right)^2. \qquad (10.1)$$

This is trivial for the terms with $j = 1$, but not for the terms with $j = 3$ or $j = 2$. Instead of (*10.1*) we shall use the formula

$$\nu_f - \nu_0 = \frac{1}{2} AK + \frac{3}{8} BK(K + 1); \qquad (10.2)$$

then

$$A = \frac{1}{ij} \left(a_1 - \frac{a_2}{2ij} \right),$$

$$B = \frac{2a_2}{3i^2 j^2}.$$

The experimentally determined values of a_1 and a_2 and the corresponding values of A and B are shown in the following table.

	a_1	a_2	A	B
$^3D_3$	598.9	40.3	56.86	0.244
$^3D_2$	453.5	27.1	64.41	0.369
$^3D_1$	−235.1	25.4	−68.2	1.38
$^3P_2$	676.1	66.3	96	0.903
$^3P_1$	571.1	−54.3	165	−2.96

The values of a_2 are certainly correct to within 10%. The distances of the fine-structure levels being very large, perturbations of the second order are not to be expected; the fact that the separations can be represented by (10.2) allows us to exclude this possibility altogether. Let us first consider the three ^3D terms. For β^2 one derives the value 0.066. We use the formula

$$B = \frac{1}{j(2j-1)} \overline{(3\cos^2\vartheta - 1)}_{j,\,j} \left(\overline{\frac{1}{r^3}}\right) \frac{Q}{(2i-1)\,i} \times 7.9$$

and substitute the values for $3\cos^2\vartheta - 1$ calculated in Section 9. It follows that

$$B_3 : B_2 : B_1 = \frac{4/7}{15} : \frac{(2/7)\,1.066}{6} : \frac{1/5}{1} = 0.244 : 0.326 : 1.28,$$

in rather good agreement with the experimental values for these ratios. In Section 19 we shall give a more accurate discussion of the B values.

We shall calculate Q from the value B_3. There are several reasons why this term is believed to give the most reliable results. First, the deviations from the interval rule are very large for $^3D_3$; second, there are 7 possible f-values, with the result that a very accurate check of (10.2) is possible; and, finally, the relativistic corrections for this term will be small.

The multiplet splitting is 2400 cm^{-1}. It follows that

$$\left(\overline{\frac{1}{r^3}}\right) = \frac{2400/2.911}{5 \times 61} \approx 2.7$$

(we use the value $Z = 61$, which perhaps will be somewhat too large). For Q we find

$$Q = +6.3.$$

Let us now consider the P terms. Here $\beta^2 = 0.05$. For the ratio of the B values we find

$$B_2:B_1 = 1:(-2.55) = 0.903:(-2.30).$$

The agreement is somewhat less satisfactory; it is to be expected that in this case the relativistic corrections will be rather important. We calculate Q from B_2. The multiplet splitting is 5189, hence

$$\left(\frac{1}{r^3}\right) = \frac{5189/2.911}{3 \times 67} = 8.8,$$

which leads to $\qquad\qquad Q = 4.1.$

The agreement with the value calculated from $^3D_3$ is not very good, and we shall see in Section 19 that it is not improved by taking into account relativistic corrections. In the same section we also discuss the possible causes of the discrepancy. Here we only point out that it is hardly to be expected that the large spin-orbit interactions occurring in this case should not give rise to perturbations of the configuration. In our opinion these discrepancies by no means cast doubt on the reality of the quadrupole moment; but they do make the value of the moment somewhat uncertain. We believe the value deduced from $^3D_3$ to be considerably more reliable than the value obtained from $^3P_2$, $^3P_1$. The multiplet splitting for the ^3D terms is smaller, and the same will presumably hold for the configuration perturbations; moreover, the satisfactory agreement that exists between the three ^3D terms makes it probable that the configuration is not appreciably perturbed.

At the time this paper was written, Eu and Cp were the only elements about which accurate data were available. Since that time Schüler and Schmidt have given a detailed account of the deviations from the interval rule in Hg, Cu, and Bi and have communicated preliminary values for the quadrupole moment of As. The results are given in the following table.

	i	μ	Q	
Cu_{63}	3/2	2.4	-0.3×10^{-24}	*(49)*
Cu_{65}	3/2	2.6	-0.3×10^{-24}	
As_{75}	3/2	0.5	$+0.2 \times 10^{-24}$	*(49)*
Bi_{209}	9/2	3.6	-0.4×10^{-24}	*(48)*
Hg_{201}	3/2	70.5	0.5×10^{-24}	*(46)*

11. Relativistic theory of s, l configurations

Following Breit and Wills (6) we shall now give a relativistic treatment of s, l configurations. For the s-electron there are two possible
states; let the corresponding wave functions be denoted by $s_{1/2}$ and
$s_{-(1/2)}$. The possible states for the l-electron can be divided into two
groups: states with $j = l + \frac{1}{2}$, and states with $j = l - \frac{1}{2}$. For the
corresponding wave functions we write $l_m^{l+(1/2)}$ and $l_m^{l-(1/2)}$ respectively. A state with total angular momentum $l + 1$ and $m = l + 1$
can be realized in one way only; the corresponding wave function is

$$^3L_{l+1}^{l+1} = s_{(1/2)}\, l_{l+(1/2)}^{l+(1/2)}. \tag{11.1}$$

In the same way there is only one state with total angular momentum $l - 1$ and $m = l - 1$; the wave function is

$$^3L_{l-1}^{l-1} = \frac{1}{\sqrt{2l}}[s_{(1/2)}\, l_{l-(3/2)}^{l-(1/2)} - \sqrt{2l-1}\, s_{-1/2}\, l_{l-(1/2)}^{l-(1/2)}.] \tag{11.2}$$

A state with $j = l$ and $m = l$, however, occurs twice. Introducing
the notation $(\frac{1}{2}, l + \frac{1}{2})_l^l$ and $(\frac{1}{2}, l - \frac{1}{2})_l^l$ for the wave functions,
we have

$$\left(\frac{1}{2}, l - \frac{1}{2}\right)_l^l = s_{1/2}\, l_{l-(1/2)}^{l-(1/2)}, \tag{11.3}$$

$$\left(\frac{1}{2}, l + \frac{1}{2}\right)_l^l = \frac{1}{\sqrt{2l+2}}[s_{1/2} l_{l-(1/2)}^{l+(1/2)} - \sqrt{2l+1}\, s_{-1/2}\, l_{l-(1/2)}^{l+(1/2)}]. \tag{11.4}$$

The last formula contains a sign convention that will be followed
throughout our further calculations. The sign of the functions
$(\frac{1}{2}, l + \frac{1}{2})_m^l$ is then fixed by the condition that the matrix elements
of the total angular momentum must have the "standard form"
(Section 1).

As long as the interaction of the electrons is neglected, the functions (11.3) and (11.4) are eigenfunctions. In consequence of the
interaction the functions $(\frac{1}{2}, l + \frac{1}{2})_l^l$ and $(\frac{1}{2}, l - \frac{1}{2})_l^l$ will be mixed and
the real wave functions will be of the form

$$\Psi_l = c_1 \left(\frac{1}{2}, l + \frac{1}{2}\right)_l^l + c_2 \left(\frac{1}{2}, l - \frac{1}{2}\right)_l^l. \tag{11.5}$$

We determine the values c_1, c_2 using a non-relativistic approximation. We shall approximate $l_m^{l+1/2}$ and $l_m^{l-1/2}$ by linear combinations of products of orbital wave functions l_m and spin functions $\sigma_{\pm 1/2}$. These approximate expressions are:

$$l_{l+(1/2)}^{l+(1/2)} = l_l \, \sigma_{1/2},$$

$$l_{l-(1/2)}^{l+(1/2)} = \frac{1}{\sqrt{2l+1}} \left(\sqrt{2l} \, l_{l-1} \sigma_{1/2} + l_l \sigma_{-1/2} \right),$$

$$l_{l-(1/2)}^{l-(1/2)} = \frac{1}{\sqrt{2l+1}} \left(l_{l-1} \sigma_{1/2} - \sqrt{2l} \, l_l \sigma_{-1/2} \right).$$

With

$$c_1 = \sqrt{\frac{l+1}{2l+1}}, \qquad c_2 = -\sqrt{\frac{l}{2l+1}}$$

one finds

$$\Psi = \frac{1}{\sqrt{2}} \, l_l \left(s_{-1/2} \sigma_{1/2} - s_{1/2} \sigma_{-1/2} \right) = \Psi_s,$$

whereas

$$c_1 = \sqrt{\frac{l}{2l+1}}, \qquad c_2 = \sqrt{\frac{l+1}{2l+1}}$$

leads to

$$\Psi = \frac{1}{\sqrt{l+1}} \, l_{l-1} S_1 - \sqrt{\frac{l}{l+1}} \, l_l S_0,$$

with

$$s_{1/2} \sigma_{1/2} = S_1$$

and

$$\frac{1}{\sqrt{2}} \left(s_{1/2} \sigma_{-1/2} + s_{-1/2} \sigma_{1/2} \right) = S_0.$$

These expressions correspond to the case of Russell-Saunders coupling. If we put for ^3L_l

$$c_1 = \sin(\vartheta_0 - \vartheta), \qquad c_2 = \cos(\vartheta_0 - \vartheta);$$

for ^1L_l

$$c_1 = \cos(\vartheta_0 - \vartheta), \qquad c_2 = -\sin(\vartheta_0 - \vartheta); \qquad (11.6)$$

and take ϑ_0 to be

$$\vartheta_0 = \text{arc tan} \sqrt{\frac{l}{l+1}}, \qquad (11.7)$$

then ϑ will be zero in the case of Russell-Saunders coupling.

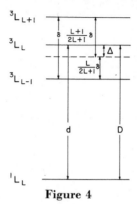

Figure 4

In determining ϑ we will follow Wolfe (43). Let us assume that the position of fine-structure levels is as shown in Figure 4, the broken line being the position of ^3L_l calculated by means of the Landé rule; then

$$\sin^2 \vartheta = \frac{\Delta}{d}. \qquad (11.8)$$

Wolfe does not only take into account the interaction of the l-orbit and the spin of the l-electron, but also the interaction of the l-orbit and the spin of the s-electron. The first-mentioned interaction is much larger than the second one; it may be expressed in terms of one constant, C_2; in the same way the second interaction can be characterized by a constant C_3. According to Wolfe,

$$C_2 + C_3 = \frac{\delta}{2l+1},$$

$$C_2 - C_3 = [\Delta D/l(l+1)]^{1/2}.$$

Usually only C_2 is taken into account, and one arrives at the conclusion that the theory of intermediate coupling applies only when

$$\frac{\delta}{2l+1} = \left[\frac{\Delta D}{l(l+1)}\right]^{1/2}. \qquad (11.9)$$

But the interaction of *l*-orbit and *s*-spin certainly exists, and as long as no unreasonably large values for C_3 are found, the fact that (*11.9*) is not strictly fulfilled is no reason to doubt the validity of (*11.8*). On the other hand, one must not forget that Wolfe's equations contain as many constants as there are independent separations, which makes it impossible to check the correctness of the assumptions. It would be useful to calculate the constant C_3 theoretically; the term with C_3 being a rather small correction, a rough calculation would be sufficient.

Finally we remark that according to Wolfe's theory the doublet splitting of a single *l*-electron is not given by δ but by $(2l + 1)C_2$. Denoting this splitting by δ_{rel}, we can then write

$$\delta_{\text{rel}} = \frac{C_2}{C + C_3} \delta_{\text{exp}}.$$

12. Solutions of Dirac's equations in a central field of force

Having determined the constants c_1 and c_2, we can calculate the mean value of $(3 \cos^2 \vartheta - 1)/r^3$ and of H_z.

In doing this we make use of the explicit expressions for the solutions of Dirac's equations in a central field of force. We use the solutions in the form given by Bethe (*2*), apart from the sign, which is chosen in agreement with the convention established in Section 11.

$$\left. \begin{aligned} j &= l + \frac{1}{2} \\ m &= l + \frac{1}{2} \end{aligned} \right\}$$

$$u_1 = if \sqrt{\frac{1}{2l+3}} \; Y_{l+1}^l$$

$$u_2 = if \sqrt{\frac{2l+2}{2l+3}} \; Y_{l+1}^{l+1} \qquad (12.1)$$

$$u_3 = g \; Y_l^l$$

$$u_4 = 0$$

$$j = l + \frac{1}{2} \Bigg\}$$
$$m = l - \frac{1}{2} \Bigg\}$$

$$u_1 = - if \sqrt{\frac{2}{2l+3}} \ Y_{l+1}^{l-1}$$

$$u_2 = - if \sqrt{\frac{2l+1}{2l+3}} \ Y_{l+1}^{l}$$

$$u_3 = - g \sqrt{\frac{2l}{2l+1}} \ Y_{l}^{l-1}$$

$$u_4 = + g \sqrt{\frac{1}{2l+1}} \ Y_{l}^{l}$$

(12.2)

$$j = l - \frac{1}{2} \Bigg\}$$
$$m = l - \frac{1}{2} \Bigg\}$$

$$u_1 = - if \ Y_{l-1}^{l-1}$$

$$u_2 = 0$$

$$u_3 = - g \sqrt{\frac{1}{2l+1}} \ Y_{l}^{l-1}$$

$$u_4 = - g \sqrt{\frac{2l}{2l+1}} \ Y_{l}^{l}$$

(12.3)

Here, f and g are functions of r only.

The functions $\chi_1 = rf$ and $\chi_2 = rg$ satisfy the equations

$$\frac{d\chi}{dr} + k \frac{\chi_1}{r} = \frac{mc}{\hbar} \left(1 - \frac{E - \Phi}{E_0} \right) \chi_2,$$

$$\frac{d\chi_2}{dr} - k \frac{\chi_2}{r} = \frac{mc}{\hbar} \left(1 + \frac{E - \Phi}{E_0} \right) \chi_1.$$

(12.4)

Here, $k = l + 1$ for $j = l + \frac{1}{2}$; $k = - l$ for $j = l - \frac{1}{2}$; $E_0 = mc^2$; and Φ is the potential energy ($\Phi = - Ze^2/r$ for a Coulomb field).

Following Breit and Wills we shall characterize the quantities relating to the state $j = l + \frac{1}{2}$ by a single prime, and those relating to the state $j = l - \frac{1}{2}$ by a double prime; then

$$k' = l + 1, \qquad j' = l + \frac{1}{2},$$

$$k'' = -l, \qquad j'' = l - \frac{1}{2}.$$

We now take $\hbar/mc$ as unit length and set

$$\frac{E}{E_0} = P, \qquad \frac{\Phi}{E} = -V;$$

then (*12.4*) reduces to

$$\frac{d\chi_1}{dr} + k\,\frac{\chi_1}{r} = (1 - P - V)\,\chi_2,$$

$$\frac{d\chi_2}{dr} - k\,\frac{\chi_2}{r} = (1 + P + V)\,\chi_1. \qquad (12.5)$$

For a Coulomb field

$$V = Z\alpha/r.$$

We apply these equations to a valency electron moving in the field of the nucleus and of the core of the atom. The ionization energy will be of the same order of magnitude as for a hydrogen atom, and $P - 1$ will thus be of the order α^2, which is very small compared with unity. In the neighborhood of the nucleus the potential energy is of the form

$$-V = -(Z\alpha/r - C_a).$$

The screening constant C_a may be written as $Z\alpha/r_s$, where r_s is a certain average radius. In our units, r_s will be a large number. For $r \ll r_s$ we can now neglect C_a and $P - 1$ altogether.

Equations (*12.5*) reduce to

$$\frac{d\chi_1}{dr} + k\,\frac{\chi_1}{r} = -\frac{Z\alpha}{r}\,\chi_2,$$

$$\frac{d\chi_2}{dr} - k\,\frac{\chi_2}{r} = \left(2 + \frac{Z\alpha}{r}\right)\chi_1. \qquad (12.6)$$

These equations can be solved in terms of Bessel functions; the solution is obtained most easily by eliminating χ_2. One finds

$$\chi_1 = CZ\alpha J_{2\rho}(2\sqrt{2Z\alpha r}),$$

$$\chi_2 = C\left[\sqrt{2Z\alpha r}\, J_{2\rho+1} - (\rho + k)\, J_{2\rho}\right], \tag{12.7}$$

with

$$\rho = \sqrt{k^2 - Z^2\alpha^2}.$$

The first terms of an expansion in powers of r are

$$\chi_1 = C(Z\alpha)^{\rho+1}\, \frac{(2r)^\rho}{\Gamma(2\rho + 1)},$$

$$\chi_2 = -\, C(\rho + k)(Z\alpha)^\rho\, \frac{(2r)^\rho}{\Gamma(2\rho + 1)} \tag{12.8}$$

For large values of $\sqrt{2Z\alpha r}$, on the other hand, the Bessel functions can be expanded in an asymptotic series. The term of highest order in the series for χ_2 is

$$\chi_2 \approx C\left(\frac{1}{\pi\sqrt{2Z\alpha r}}\right)^{1/2}\left[\sqrt{2Z\alpha r}\cos\left(2\sqrt{2Z\alpha r} - \rho\pi - \frac{3}{4}\pi\right)\right]. \tag{12.9}$$

We now introduce the assumption that there exists a value r_1 in the neighborhood of which on the one hand the solutions (12.7) are a good approximation, and on the other hand the Bessel functions are given with a fair degree of accuracy by the first term of their asymptotic expansions.

For large values of r the relativistic corrections will be negligible, and χ_2 will be a solution of the nonrelativistic Schrödinger equation, χ_1 being given by

$$\chi_1 = \frac{1}{2}\left(\frac{d\chi_2}{dr} - k\,\frac{\chi_2}{r}\right).$$

In order to obtain a better idea of the dependence of the relativistic corrections on the value of r we deduce a rigorous equation for χ_2 by eliminating χ_1 from (12.5). Setting

$$\chi_1 = \sqrt{P + V - 1}\; v_1,$$

$$\chi_2 = \sqrt{P + V + 1}\; v_2, \tag{12.10}$$

one finds that

$$v_1^{(\prime\prime)} + \left[(P + V)^2 - 1 - \frac{k(k+1)}{r^2} \right.$$

$$\left. + \frac{\frac{1}{2}V^{(\prime\prime)} - (k/r)V^{(\prime)}}{P + V - 1} - \frac{3}{4}\frac{(V^{(\prime)})^2}{(P+V-1)^2} \right] v_1 = 0, \qquad (12.11)$$

where (') and ('') denote the first and second derivatives with respect to r, and

$$v_2^{(\prime\prime)} + \left[(P + V)^2 - 1 - \frac{k(k-1)}{r^2} \right.$$

$$\left. + \frac{\frac{1}{2}V^{(\prime\prime)} + (k/r)V^{(\prime)}}{P + V + 1} - \frac{3}{4}\frac{(V^{(\prime)})^2}{(P+V+1)^2} \right] v_2 = 0. \qquad (12.12)$$

In calculating the relativistic corrections in first approximation one usually considers the term with V^2 and the term $\frac{1}{2}(k/r)V^{(\prime)}$. If $V = Z\alpha/r$, then (12.12) becomes

$$v_2^{(\prime\prime)} + \left[\left(P + \frac{Z\alpha}{r}\right)^2 - 1 - \frac{k(k-1)}{r^2} \right.$$

$$\left. + \frac{rZ\alpha(1-k)(1+P) + Z\alpha^2(\frac{1}{4} - k)}{(P + Z\alpha/r + 1)^2 r^4} \right] v_2 = 0.$$

Taking into account that $k(k-1) = l(l+1)$, one sees that the difference between this equation and the Schrödinger equation consists in the term $(Z\alpha/r)^2$ and the term with r^4 in the denominator. For $Z\alpha = 0.5$ and $r = 5$, for instance, these two terms are already very small. If there exists a value r_1 with the properties mentioned above, then for $r \geq r_1$ the relativistic corrections will be negligible. On the other hand it will be possible to set

$$\chi_2 = \sqrt{2}\, v_2. \qquad (12.13)$$

For larger values of r we can now approximate v_2 by a Wentzel-Kramers-Brillouin (W-K-B) function. Outside the atomic core (for very large values of r) this function may be fitted to the rigorous solution for the Coulomb field, with charge number $Z_0 = 1 + z$ (z = degree of ionization). We thus obtain a solution that is built up in the following way.

$0 \leq r \leq r_1$	$r \sim r_1$	$r \geq r_1$	$r \gg r_1$
Bessel functions (relativistic)	Asymptotic exp. of Bessel functions	Nonrelativistic WKB solution	Rigorous solution

The solution for $r < r_1$ does not depend on the energy.

13. Calculation of the normalization integral

We now deduce a formula for the normalization integral of this wave function. In doing this we shall neglect the contribution of the interval $0 \leq r \leq r_1$. We consider the nonrelativistic Schrödinger equation

$$w^{(\prime\prime)} + \left[2(P - 1) + 2V - \frac{l(l+1)}{r^2} \right] w = w^{(\prime\prime)} + p^2 w = 0. \quad (13.1)$$

Let P have an arbitrary value, and let w be the solution that is regular at infinity; for a given P the function w is determined apart from a multiplicative constant. We differentiate this equation with respect to P and find, putting $dw/dP = w_P$, that

$$w_P^{(\prime\prime)} + \left[2(P - 1) + 2V - \frac{l(l+1)}{r^2} \right] w_P = -2w. \quad (13.2)$$

It then follows that

$$\frac{d}{dr} (w^{(\prime)} w_P - w_P^{(\prime)} w) = w^{(\prime\prime)} w_P - w_P^{(\prime\prime)} w = 2w^2.$$

Integrating this equation from $r = r_1$ to $r = \infty$ we obtain

$$\int_{r_1}^{\infty} w^2 dr = -\frac{1}{2} (w^{(\prime)} w_P - w_P^{(\prime)} w)_{r=r_1} = \frac{1}{2} w^2 \frac{\partial}{\partial P} \left(\frac{w^{(\prime)}}{w} \right)_{r=r_1}. \quad (13.3)$$

If P is an eigenvalue, then the value of $w^{(\prime)}/w$ is equal to the value $v_2^{(\prime)}/v_2$, where v_2 is the solution of the relativistic wave equation that is regular for $r = 0$ and which does not depend on P.

It can be proved that the quantity

$$\vartheta = \text{arc tan} (w^{(\prime)}/w)$$

is a monotonic function of P. If the quantum number increases by

1, then ϑ increases by π, but no general expression can be given for the dependence of ϑ on P.

Let us now consider a W-K-B approximation for the function w. It will be of the form

$$w = \frac{K}{\sqrt{p}} \sin\left[\int_{r_1}^{r} p\,dr - \psi(P) \right]. \qquad (13.4)$$

From this we obtain

$$\int_{r_1}^{\infty} w^2 dr = \frac{1}{2} K^2 \frac{d\psi}{dP}.$$

In deducing this expression derivatives of p with respect to P were neglected in accordance with the fact that for $r < r_1$ the solutions of the wave equation do not depend on the values of P. If P increases, ψ also will increase, and the eigenvalues can be determined from the equation

$$\psi = \psi_0 + n\pi;$$

hence we may also write

$$\int_{r_1}^{\infty} w^2 dr = \frac{\pi}{2} K^2 \frac{dn}{dP}. \qquad (13.5)$$

There will now exist a simple functional relation between n and P, and it will be permissible to calculate the value of dn/dP by means of an interpolation formula for P as a function of n. Taking into account that

$$\int_{0}^{\infty} (|\chi_1|^2 + |\chi_2|^2)\,dr \approx 2 \int_{0}^{\infty} w^2 dr$$

and that according to (12.9) and (12.13)

$$K = C\sqrt{\frac{Z\alpha}{\pi}}, \qquad (13.6)$$

we find

$$N = \int_{0}^{\infty} (|\chi_1|^2 + |\chi_2|^2)\,dr = C^2 Z\alpha \bigg/ \frac{dP}{dn}.$$

Denoting by E_R the energy measured in units $Rh = \frac{1}{2}\alpha^2 mc^2$, we obtain

$$P - 1 = \frac{1}{2}\alpha^2 E_R,$$

$$N = C^2 \frac{2Z}{\alpha} \Big/ \frac{dE_R}{dn}.$$

For a normalized wave function the constant C will be given by

$$C^2 = \frac{\alpha}{2Z} \frac{dE_R}{dn}. \tag{13.7}$$

Let us consider the nature of the dependence of n and E_R somewhat more closely. Suppose for a moment that for $r \geq r_1$ the field is a Coulomb field with charge number $1 + z$. In that case the phase $\psi(P)$ of the function w would be given by $n^*\pi + b$, where b is a constant and where the relation between E_R and n^* is

$$E_R = -\frac{(1 + z)^2}{n^{*2}}. \tag{13.8}$$

The difference between this expression and the true phase will in first approximation be independent of the energy, when the core of the atom is small compared with the dimensions of the "orbit." In higher approximation it will be possible to expand this difference in ascending powers of E_R. We then find

$$\psi = n\pi + \psi_0 = n^*\pi + b + cE_R + \cdots.$$

Omitting the term containing E_R, we have

$$n = n^* + \delta_1$$

and

$$\frac{dE}{dn} = \frac{dE}{dn^*} = 2 \frac{Z_0^2}{n^{*3}}, \tag{13.9}$$

whence

$$C^2 = \frac{\alpha}{Z} \frac{Z_0^2}{n^{*3}}. \tag{13.10}$$

Taking into account the term cE_R corresponds to using the Ritz correction.

When dE_R/dn is determined by means of the Rydberg-Ritz formula, the theoretical foundation of (13.10) seems to be identical with that of the Rydberg-Ritz formula itself. In one respect, however, this is not completely correct. In our deduction of the Rydberg-Ritz formula it is assumed that the wave function for $r < r_1$ does not depend on E_R, but it is not assumed that the influence of screening can be neglected. If the screening is taken into account, the value of K, and therefore also the value of C, will be slightly modified. Calculations of K were carried out by Fermi and his collaborators, using a potential determined by the statistical method. The corrections are not very large, however, and they will not be taken into account here.

A formula equivalent to (13.10) has been derived by Goudsmit; a proof of this equation and of the somewhat more general (13.7) has been given by Fermi and Segré (16). The formulation of the proof given above was the result of a discussion with Professor Kramers.

14. *The doublet separation*

In Section 12 we have seen that in the neighborhood of r_1 the function χ_2 is given approximately as

$$\chi_2' \approx C' \left(\frac{1}{\pi \sqrt{2Z\alpha r}} \right)^{1/2} \left[\sqrt{2Z\alpha r} \cos \left(2\sqrt{2Z\alpha r} - \rho'\pi - \frac{3}{4}\pi \right) \right]$$

$$(14.1)$$

for the state

$$j' = l + \frac{1}{2},$$

and as

$$\chi_2'' \approx C'' \left(\frac{1}{\pi \sqrt{2Z\alpha r}} \right)^{1/2} \left[\sqrt{2Z\alpha r} \cos \left(2\sqrt{2Z\alpha r} - \rho''\pi - \frac{3}{4}\pi \right) \right]$$

$$(14.2)$$

for the state $j'' = l - \frac{1}{2}$. Since $\rho' - \rho'' \approx 1$, these functions will be approximately identical if we choose

$$C'' \approx -C'.$$

The remaining phase difference between χ_2' and χ_2'' is $(\rho' - \rho'' - 1)\pi$. Hence the energy difference of those two states will be

$$(\rho' - \rho'' - 1)\,\pi \frac{dP}{d\psi} = \frac{1}{2}\,\alpha^2(\rho' - \rho'' - 1)\frac{dE_R}{dn}.$$

The separation in cm^{-1} will now be given by

$$\delta_{rel} = (\rho' - \rho'' - 1) \frac{dE_R}{dn} R. \qquad (14.3)$$

Neglecting higher powers of $(Z\alpha)^2$ we find

$$\rho' = \sqrt{(l+1)^2 - Z^2\alpha^2} = l + 1 - \frac{(Z\alpha)^2}{2l+2},$$

$$\rho'' = \sqrt{l^2 - Z^2\alpha^2} = l - \frac{(Z\alpha)^2}{2l},$$

$$\rho' - \rho'' - 1 = \frac{Z^2\alpha^2}{2l(l+1)}.$$

Writing

$$E_R = -\frac{Z_0^2}{n^{*2}}$$

we obtain

$$\delta = \frac{dn^*}{dn} \frac{Z^2 Z_0^2}{n^{*3} l(l+1)} R\alpha^2. \qquad (14.4)$$

If the Rydberg formula is valid, $dn^*/dn = 1$, and (14.4) reduces to the well-known Landé formula. The formula (13.10) was proposed by Goudsmit (20) in analogy to the formula of Landé. We now see that the theoretical foundations of the two formulas are the same. At the same time we have found correction factors of Landé's formula; namely, a relativistic factor,

$$H = (\rho' - \rho'' - 1) \Big/ \frac{Z^2\alpha^2}{2l(l+1)},$$

and a "Ritz correction" factor,

$$\delta_{rel} = H \frac{dn^*}{dn} \delta \text{ Landé}. \qquad (14.5)$$

The fact that doublet separations for terms with small n^* in one- and two-electron spectra of heavy elements can be represented with an accuracy of 10 or 20% by means of (14.4), when the total nuclear charge Z is diminished by 2 for a p-state and by 10 for a d-state, is therefore a strong argument in favor of the validity of our formulas. The numbers "2" and "10" are somewhat arbitrary, but for heavy nuclei this is of little importance. Better values of the screening corrections might be obtained by the statistical method.

It would also be interesting to see how far the corrections by which (14.4) differs from the ordinary Landé formula lead to a material improvement of the agreement between theory and experiment.

It was pointed out by Breit and Wills that the normalization integrals for the states j' and j'' will be slightly different from each other because of the energy difference between these states. From (13.7) one can deduce that the difference between the C values for the normalized wave functions is given by

$$C'^2 - C''^2 = \frac{\alpha}{2Z} \frac{d^2 E_R}{dn^2} (\rho' - \rho'' - 1)$$

or, assuming $dn^*/dn = 1$, by

$$\frac{C'^2 - C''^2}{C'^2} = - \frac{3Z^2 \alpha^2}{2l(l+1)n^*}.$$

Although one can hardly expect that this formula will be strictly valid, one may nevertheless expect it to give an idea of the possible order of magnitude of such corrections. It is sometimes useful to write the formula for the doublet separation in the form

$$\delta_{\mathrm{rel}} = HZ \left(l + \frac{1}{2} \right) \left(\frac{1}{r^3} \right)_{kl} R\alpha^2; \qquad (14.6)$$

the quantity $(\overline{1/r^3})_{kl}$ will be defined in the next section.

15. Calculation of the mean value of $(3 \cos^2 \vartheta - 1)/r^3$

Using the results derived in the previous sections we can now calculate the mean value of $(3 \cos^2 \vartheta - 1)/r^3$. We assume that only the values $r < r_1$ will contribute appreciably to this average. Since the calculations do not offer any points of interest, we shall confine ourselves to stating the results.

We find

$$\left(\frac{3 \cos^2 \vartheta - 1}{r^3} \right)_{j,j} = - \frac{2l}{2l+3} \left(\frac{1}{r^3} \right)^{',\,'}, \qquad j = l+1,$$

$$\left(\frac{3 \cos^2 \vartheta - 1}{r^3} \right)_{j,j} = - \frac{2(l-1)(l+1)(2l-3)}{l(2l-1)(2l+1)} \left(\frac{1}{r^3} \right)^{'',\,''}, \quad j = l-1,$$

$$\left(\frac{3\cos^2\vartheta - 1}{r^3}\right)_{j,j} = -\left[c_1^2 \frac{(2l-1)(l+2)2l}{(l+1)(2l+1)(2l+3)}\left(\frac{1}{r^3}\right)^{',''} j = l,\right.$$

$$\left. + c_2^2 \frac{2(l-1)}{2l+1}\left(\frac{1}{r^3}\right)^{'',''} - \frac{12\,c_1c_2\sqrt{l/(l+1)}}{(2l+1)(2l+3)}\left(\frac{1}{r^3}\right)^{',''}\right],$$

with

$$\left(\frac{1}{r^3}\right)^{',''} = \int_0^\infty [|\chi_1'|^2 + |\chi_2'|^2]\frac{1}{r^3}\,dr,$$

$$\left(\frac{1}{r^3}\right)^{'',''} = \int_0^\infty [|\chi_1''|^2 + |\chi_2''|^2]\frac{1}{r^3}\,dr,$$

$$\left(\frac{1}{r^3}\right)^{',''} = \int_0^\infty [\chi_1'\chi_2'' + \chi_2'\chi_1'']\frac{1}{r^3}\,dr.$$

These quantities may be written as

$$\left(\frac{1}{r^3}\right)^{',''} = R'\left(\frac{1}{r^3}\right)_{kl},$$

$$\left(\frac{1}{r^3}\right)^{'',''} = R''\left(\frac{1}{r^3}\right)_{kl},$$

$$\left(\frac{1}{r^3}\right)^{',''} = S\left(\frac{1}{r^3}\right)_{kl},$$

where R', R'', and S are certain relativistic correction factors. Formulas and numerical values are given in Section 17, and

$$\left(\frac{1}{r^3}\right)_{kl} = C^2 \frac{Z^2\alpha^2}{l(l+\frac{1}{2})(l+1)} = \alpha^3 Z \frac{dE_R}{dn}/l(l+1)(2l+1).$$

Here the unit of length is still $\hbar/mc$. Introducing $a_H = \hbar/\alpha mc$ as the unit of length, we have

$$\left(\frac{1}{r^3}\right)_{kl} = \frac{Z}{l(l+1)(2l+1)}\frac{dE_R}{dn}.$$

Here normalization corrections were not taken into account. If we set $R' = R'' = S = 1$ and insert for c_1 and c_2 the values for Russell-

Saunders coupling our formulas reduce to the expressions derived in Section 9.

Finally we repeat here the fundamental formula

$$(\Delta_f \nu)_{el} = B\left(\frac{3}{8} K(K+1) - \frac{1}{2} i(i+1) j(j+1)\right),$$

with

$$- (2j-1) jB = \left(\frac{3 \cos^2 \vartheta - 1}{r^3}\right)_{j, \, j} \frac{Q}{(2i-1)i} \times 7.9 \times 10^{-3} \text{ cm}^{-1}.$$

16. Formulas for the magnetic interaction

Breit and Wills have derived the following formulas.

Let A be the constant in the equation

$$(\Delta_f \nu)_m = \frac{A}{2} K.$$

Then we have

$$A = \frac{a(s)}{2(l+1)} + \frac{2l+1}{2(l+1)} a', \qquad\qquad j = l+1,$$

$$A = -\frac{a(s)}{2l} + \frac{2l+1}{2l} a'', \qquad\qquad (j = l-1)$$

$$l(l+1) A = \frac{1}{2} [(l+1) c_2^2 - lc_1^2] a(s) \qquad\qquad (j = l)$$

$$+ \frac{1}{2} l (2l+3) c_1^2 a' + \frac{1}{2} (2l-1)(l+1) c_2^2 a'' + 2c_1 c_2 \sqrt{l(l+1)} \, a'''.$$

Here

$$\left.\begin{array}{l} a' \\ a'' \end{array}\right\} = \gamma \frac{2l(l+1)}{j(j+1)} \left(\frac{1}{r^3}\right)_{kl} F \times 1.585 \times 10^{-3} \text{ cm}^{-1},$$

$$a''' = -\gamma \frac{1}{2l+1} \left(\frac{1}{r^3}\right)_{kl} G \times 1.585 \times 10^{-3} \text{ cm}^{-1},$$

$$a(s) = \frac{8}{3} Z \frac{dE_R}{dn} F \times 1.585 \times 10^{-3} \text{ cm}^{-1},$$

where a', a'' and $a(s)$ are the constants for one electron in the states $j = l + \frac{1}{2}, j = l - \frac{1}{2}$, and $l = 0$; F and G are relativistic corrections.

16. Relativistic corrections

In this section we give formulas and a table for the relativistic corrections:

$$R = \frac{l(l+1)(2l+1)}{\rho(\rho^2-1)(4\rho^2-1)}[3k(k+1)-\rho^2+1],$$

$$S = \frac{2l(l+1)\sin\pi(\rho-\rho''-1)}{\pi Z^2\alpha^2}\left\{\frac{3(\rho'+k')}{8(1+\rho'')-4l-2}\right.$$

$$+\frac{3(\rho''+k'')}{8(1+\rho')+4l+2}-\frac{1}{2}\frac{\rho'+\rho''-1}{\rho'+\rho''+2}$$

$$\left.-\frac{6[Z^2\alpha^2+(\rho'+k')(\rho''+k'')]}{3(2l+3)(2l-1)-16Z^2\alpha^2}\right\},$$

$$H = \frac{2l(l+1)}{Z^2\alpha^2}(\rho'-\rho''-1),$$

$$G = \frac{2l(l+1)\sin\pi(\rho'-\rho''-1)}{\pi Z^2\alpha^2},$$

$$F = \frac{k(2k+1)(2l+1)}{\rho(4\rho^2-1)} = \frac{4j(j+\frac{1}{2})(j+1)}{\rho(4\rho^2-1)},$$

$$j = l+\frac{1}{2}, \qquad\qquad k = l+1,$$

$$j = l-\frac{1}{2}, \qquad\qquad k = -l,$$

$$\rho = \sqrt{k^2-Z^2\alpha^2}.$$

$l = 1, k' = 2, k'' = -1$

Z	αZ	ρ'	ρ''	H	F'	F''	G	R''	R'	S
82.2	0.6	1.9079	0.8000	1.20	1.16	2.40	1.18	—	1.35	1.74
68.5	0.5	1.9364	0.8660	1.12	1.11	1.73	1.12	—	1.23	1.42
54.8	0.4	1.9596	0.9165	1.08	1.07	1.39	1.08	—	1.14	1.24
41.1	0.3	1.9774	0.9539	1.04	1.04	1.19	1.04	—	1.07	1.13
27.4	0.2	1.9900	0.9798	1.02	1.01	1.08	1.02	—	1.03	1.05
13.7	0.1	1.9975	0.9950	1.00	1.00	1.02	1.00	—	1.01	1.01

$l = 2, k' = 3, k'' = -2$

Z	αZ	ρ'	ρ''	H	F'	F''	G	R''	R'	S
82.2	0.6	2.9394	1.9079	1.05	1.06	1.16	1.05	1.48	1.13	1.13
68.5	0.5	2.9580	1.9364	1.03	1.04	1.11	1.03	1.31	1.09	1.09
54.8	0.4	2.9732	1.9596	1.02	1.03	1.07	1.02	1.18	1.05	1.05
41.1	0.3	2.9850	1.9774	1.01	1.01	1.04	1.01	1.10	1.03	1.03
27.4	0.2	2.9933	1.9900	1.00	1.00	1.01	1.00	1.05	1.01	1.01
13.7	0.1	2.9983	1.9975	1.00	1.00	1.00	1.00	1.01	1.00	1.00

18. Discussion of the reliability of the relativistic calculations

Before applying our formulas we shall examine what deviations from our theory are to be expected. First, it is not certain that the values c_1 and c_2 calculated by means of (*11.6*) to (*11.8*) are exactly correct, since these formulas were derived by means of a calculation in which only certain first-order terms were taken into account. This difficulty is avoided in Goudsmit's method, which can also be applied to more complicated configurations. This method is based on the fact that the sum of the values of A (and also of B) for the states ^3L_l and ^1L_l is independent of the values of c_1, c_2; it can be applied with advantage to the discussion of the magnetic separations. The case is different, however, for the electric separations. The A-value for ^1L_l is usually much smaller than the value for ^3L_l, whereas the B-values are of the same order of magnitude. On the other hand a determination of B is possible only when the hyperfine structure can be measured with a high degree of precision, and the hyperfine structure must therefore be well resolved; owing to the small A-value, this condition will rarely be fulfilled for ^1L_l.

Second, it is questionable whether or not the wave function can be represented with a sufficient degree of accuracy by functions of the type considered. In reality any configuration will be perturbed, but it is difficult to estimate the order of magnitude of these perturbations.

Third, it remains to be discussed whether or not our approximation for the relativistic wave functions in a central field is sufficiently accurate. If the results so obtained are compared with the results of exact numerical calculations, if available, then a satisfactory agreement is found [see Breit (6)]. Moreover, the validity of Landé's formula for the doublet separation is an argument in favor of the validity of this approximation.

If the magnetic moment and, whenever possible, the electric quadrupole moment is calculated from the separations of a number of terms, and if these values are in agreement with each other, then these values may be considered fairly reliable. But if discrepancies are found, it will then be necessary to see whether these can be ascribed to one of the causes discussed in this section. It is clear, however, that it is impossible to test the theory very strictly and that deviations of the type discussed in Section 2 would hardly have been detected.

19. Discussion of the hyperfine structure of cassiopeium

We now apply our theory to the hyperfine structure of Cp. Let us first discuss the D terms. The fine-structure levels are shown in Figure 5.

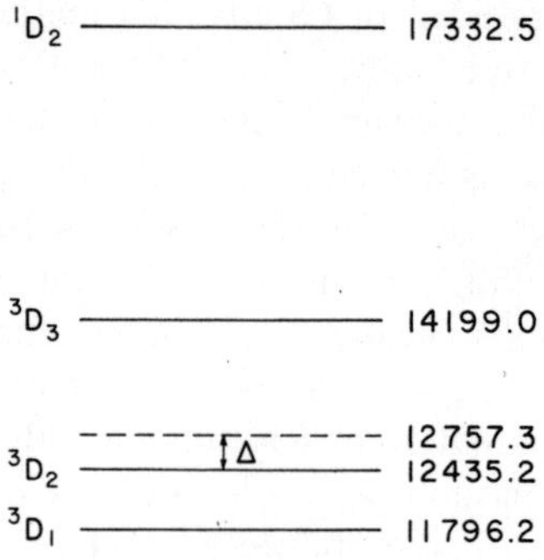

$^1D_2$ ———————— 17332.5

$^3D_3$ ———————— 14199.0

$^3D_2$ ———————— 12757.3 / 12435.2 (with Δ)

$^3D_1$ ———————— 11796.2

Figure 5

Application of Wolfe's formula gives

$$\sin^2 \vartheta = \frac{322.1}{4897.3},$$

hence

$$c_1^2 = 0.17, \qquad c_2^2 = 0.83, \qquad c_1 c_2 = 0.376.$$

Further,

$$C_2 + C_3 = 480.6,$$

$$C_2 - C_3 = 495.6,$$

We see that since C_3 is small the value of ϑ is well determined, even when C_3 is not taken into account.

For the relativistic correction factors we find (using the value $Z = 61$, which corresponds to applying a screening correction of 10 to our formulas):

$$R' = 1.07, \qquad R'' = 1.24, \qquad S = 1.07.$$

Thus we arrive at the equations for $(2j - 1)j\,B$:

$$^3D_3 \qquad 1.07 \times \frac{4}{7} \times 7.9 \times \left(\frac{1}{r^3}\right)_{kl} \times \left(\frac{Q}{21}\right) = 15 \times 0.244,$$

$$^3D_1 \qquad 1.24 \times \frac{1}{5} \times 7.9 \times \left(\frac{1}{r^3}\right)_{kl} \times \left(\frac{Q}{21}\right) = 1.38,$$

$$^3D_2 \qquad \left(\frac{4 \times 3 \times 4}{3 \times 5 \times 7} \times 1.07 \times 0.17 + \frac{2}{5} \times 0.83 \times 1.24 - \sqrt{\frac{2}{3}}\right.$$
$$\left. \times 0.376 \times \frac{12}{5 \times 7} \times 1.07\right) \times 7.9 \times \left(\frac{1}{r^3}\right)_{kl} \times \left(\frac{Q}{21}\right) = 6 \times 0.369.$$

Using the value

$$\left(\frac{1}{r^3}\right)_{kl} = \frac{2403/2.911}{5 \times 61} = 2.71,$$

we find

$$^3D_3 \qquad\qquad\qquad Q = 5.8,$$
$$^3D_2 \qquad\qquad\qquad Q = 5.6,$$
$$^3D_1 \qquad\qquad\qquad Q = 5.4^5.$$

The agreement between these values is very satisfactory.

We also discuss the magnetic part of the hyperfine structure. Introducing the notation

$$b = \gamma \left(\frac{1}{r^3}\right)_{kl} \times 1.585 \times 10^{-3}\ \mathrm{cm}^{-1},$$

we find

$$^3D_3 \qquad\qquad \frac{1}{6}\,a(s) + \frac{8}{7} \times 1.04\,b = 56.86,$$

$^3D_1$ $-\dfrac{1}{4}\,a(s) + 4 \times 1.09\,b = -68.2.$

hence

$$a(s) = 331, \qquad b = 1.8,$$

and

$$a' = 4, \qquad a'' = 9.8, \qquad a''' = -0.57.$$

For the state $^3D_2$ we now have

$$6A = \dfrac{1}{2}(3 \times 0.83 - 2 \times 0.17)\,321 + 7 \times 0.17 \times 4$$
$$+ 4.5 \times 0.83 \times 9.8 - 2\sqrt{6} \times 0.376 \times 0.57,$$

whence

$$A = 64.2,$$

which is in excellent agreement with the experimental value

$$A = 64.4.$$

From the value of b it follows that

$$\gamma = 0.42.$$

The fact that the formulas for the magnetic interaction lead to results in agreement with experimental data is of special importance since it shows that the configuration is not appreciably perturbed. It is certainly not permissible to attach much weight to the value of γ, but still it is remarkable that it is of the same order of magnitude as the value for other nuclei with $i = 7/2$; namely, La, Cs and Sb (compare Crawford and Grace) (12).

We now turn to a discussion of the P-terms. Here we have

$$\sin^2 \vartheta = \frac{490.8}{9720.1},$$

$$C_2 + C_3 = 1729.6, \qquad C_2 - C_3 = 1504.9,$$

and

$$c_1^2 = 0.1438, \qquad c_2^2 = 0.8562, \qquad c_1 c_2 = 0.351.$$

The value of C_3 does not appear unreasonably large. The relativistic correction factors are:

$$R' = 1.23, \qquad S = 1.40,$$

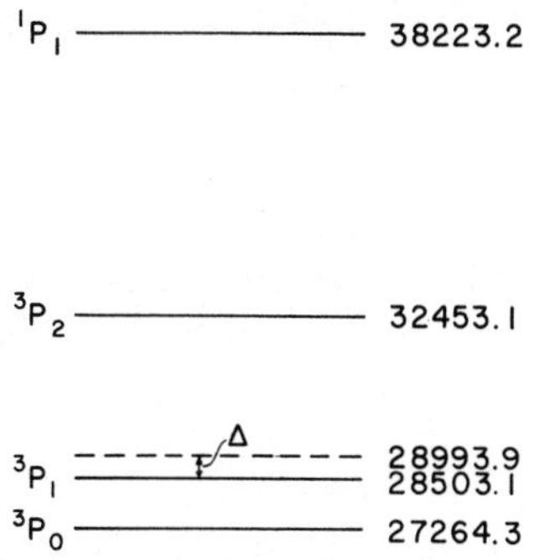

Figure 6

and we obtain the equations

$^3P_2$ $$\left(\frac{Q}{2I}\right) \times \left(\overline{\frac{1}{r^3}}\right)_{kl} \times \frac{2}{5} \times 1.23 \times 7.9 = 5.42,$$

$^3P_1$ $$\left(\frac{Q}{2I}\right) \times \left(\overline{\frac{1}{r^3}}\right)_{kl}$$

$$\times \left(0.1438 \times \frac{1}{5} \times 1.23 - 0.35 \times \frac{2}{5}\sqrt{2} \times 1.4\right) = -2.96.$$

We then obtain

$^3P_2$ $$Q = 29.2 \Big/ \left(\overline{\frac{1}{r^3}}\right)_{kl},$$

$^3P_1$ $$Q = 32.4 \Big/ \left(\overline{\frac{1}{r^3}}\right)_{kl}.$$

The agreement between these values is sufficiently good.

For

$$\delta_{\exp} = 5188.8, \qquad H = 1.12 \text{ and } (C_2 + C_3)/C_2 = 1.07$$

we find, using (14.5) and (14.6),

$$\left(\overline{\frac{1}{r^3}}\right)_{kl} = 7.3,$$

which leads to

$$^3P_2 \hspace{6cm} Q = 4.0,$$

$$^3P_1 \hspace{6cm} Q = 4.4.$$

The agreement of these values with those derived from the
D-terms is rather bad. There are several possible explanations for
this discrepancy. For example, it is possible that the configuration
is perturbed. Unfortunately the Cp-spectrum is not sufficiently well
known to permit further discussion of this question. It also seems
possible that an application of our formulas for the doublet separation is not permissible for the very large separations occurring here,
but since the effective quantum number is not known, neither can
this question be investigated any further. It may be of interest, however, to remark that if we calculate n^* from (14.4) and the known
doublet separation, a reasonable value is found. An investigation of
the magnetic separation does not offer any new point of view. A
satisfactory agreement with experimental values can be obtained
with widely differing values of b. We believe that the average value
for the D^3 states, that is,

$$Q = 5.6,$$

is the most reliable value that can be given at present.

20. *The problem of the internal conversion of nuclear energy*

Let us suppose that at $t = 0$ the nucleus is in an excited state M
with energy $\hbar\nu_M$ and that the electrons are in a state m with energy
$\hbar\nu_m$. Two different processes are now possible. The nucleus may
pass to a state N having energy $\hbar\nu_N < \hbar\nu_M$ with the emission of a
light quantum of frequency $\nu_M - \nu_N = \omega$; the energy $\hbar\omega$ may also
be used, however, to transfer the electronic system to an excited
state n with energy $\hbar\nu_n$ (such that $\nu_n - \nu_m = \omega$). In the latter case we
speak of internal conversion of nuclear energy.

The problem that now arises consists in calculating the relative
probabilities of the two processes mentioned. The formalism of
quantum mechanics gives a general method for calculating these
probabilities. To the transition NM there belong a charge density

ρ_{NM} and a current density s_{NM} of the form

$$\rho_{NM} = \rho_{NM}^0 \, e^{-i\omega t}, \qquad s_{NM} = s_{NM}^0 \, e^{-i\omega t},$$

where ρ_{NM}^0 and s_{NM}^0 do not depend on time.

The probability that a quantum with frequency ω will be emitted during the time Δt is determined by calculating through classical electrodynamics the amount of energy emitted during the time Δt by a charge density $\rho_{NM} + \rho_{NM}^{*}$ and a current density $s_{NM} + s_{NM}^{*}$ and by dividing this value by $\hbar\omega$. The probability of the second process is equal to the probability that the electronic system will carry out a transition from the state m to the state n when acted upon by the electromagnetic field corresponding to ρ_{NM} and s_{NM}.

Let us compare this problem with the problem of hyperfine structure. In the case of hyperfine structure we are concerned with the change of energy levels caused by the field produced by stationary current and charge densities; in the case of internal conversion we must calculate the probability of transitions produced by a varying current and charge.

The method of calculating the probability of the transition $(M, m) \rightarrow (N, n)$, by calculating the probability of the transition $m \rightarrow n$ of the second system under influence of the field belonging to the transition $M \rightarrow N$ of the first system, was devised by Moller (28), who based his considerations on the correspondence principle. Bethe and Fermi (3) have shown that in the case of two free electrons, which is the case originally considered by Moller, Moller's results can be deduced from quantum electrodynamics. But their considerations do not apply to the more general case, which we shall have to consider; moreover, although Moller's results are proved, one does not see very clearly why his procedure is correct. It is possible, however, to give a general proof. The most simple formulation is obtained if, following a method devised by Heisenberg (24), we make use of the fact that Maxwell's laws for the electromagnetic field are still valid in quantum mechanics. It would lead us too far, however, to give the proof here. Such a proof has recently also been given by Hulme (45).

In calculating the transitions $(M, m) \rightarrow (N, n)$ we must use the second approximation of the theory of radiation. If we also wish to determine the influence of the interaction of the nucleus and the electrons on the intensity of the radiation we must work out a third approximation. If only the first and second approximations are taken into account, the intensity of the electromagnetic radiation is not changed by this interaction. Originally it was assumed by Hulme (25) and by Mott and Taylor (40) that the probability for the emission of a light quantum must be diminished by the probability that a transition $(M, m) \rightarrow (N, n)$ takes place. Later on it was found by Taylor and Mott (41) that this assumption sometimes leads to impossible results, since it is possible to construct a model for which one would obtain a negative probability for the emission of a light quantum. They then tried to calculate the change in the number of light quanta (or, in our terminology, to determine the third approximation of the theory of radiation) and arrived at the result that, in all practical applications, this change will be negligible. Their method is as follows: they calculate the radiation emitted by the total charge density of nucleus plus electrons, this charge density being calculated in second approximation by using Moller's formulas for the interaction. It is not quite evident that this is correct, since Moller's formulas hold only in the case of conservation of energy (that is, when $\nu_n - \nu_m = \nu_M - \nu_N$). Recently, however, Moller (29) has treated the radiation emitted during the collision of two particles by an analogous method and has succeeded in showing that his results may also be deduced from quantum mechanics. His proof is very complicated, however, and an extension to more general systems would be extremely cumbersome. It is probable that, here too, application of Heisenberg's method would lead to considerable simplifications.

21. Multipole radiation

As mentioned in the Introduction, the major part of this section has been replaced by Appendix A. We shall now formulate the selection rules that hold for the electric dipole fields, magnetic dipole fields, and quadrupole fields, respectively. In our approximation these rules can be easily verified, but they also hold when the rigorous expressions are used.

Electric dipole radiation can only be emitted in transitions in which the angular momentum is changed by one unit:

$$i - \begin{vmatrix} \to i + 1 \\ \to i \\ \to i - 1 \end{vmatrix}$$

Moreover, the transition $0 \to 0$ is forbidden. The symmetry with respect to inversion must be different in the final and in the initial state.

In magnetic dipole radiation we also have

$$i - \begin{vmatrix} \to i + 1 \\ \to i \\ \to i - 1 \end{vmatrix},$$

and, again, the transition $0 \to 0$ is forbidden. Both the final and the initial state must have the same symmetry.

In electric quadrupole radiation we have

$$i - \begin{vmatrix} \to i + 2 \\ \to i + 1 \\ \to i \\ \to i - 1 \\ \to i - 2 \end{vmatrix}.$$

The transitions $0 \to 0$, $0 \to 1$, $1 \to 0$, and $\frac{1}{2} \to \frac{1}{2}$ are forbidden. The initial state and the final state must have the same symmetry. It follows that magnetic dipole radiation and electric quadrupole radiation can be emitted in the same transition.

22. The calculation of the transition probabilities

The problem of the internal conversion has now been reduced to a problem that depends only on the atomic electrons. There are, however, still a number of questions to be discussed. For instance, which are the stationary states of the atom? An excited state of the nucleus will always have been preceded by a violent perturbation— usually a radioactive disintegration (and thus a change of atomic number). Is it permissible to use in our calculations the stationary states of the new atom? Quantum mechanics gives an affirmative answer to this question; one has to take into account, however, that the atom may be in an excited or an ionized state. It is clear that any state of the new atom can be represented by a wave function $\sum c_n \psi_n$, where c_n remains constant, once the perturbation has stopped (apart from a change due to spontaneous emission of radiation). To the "disorganization" of the electrons, which would take place in classical mechanics, there corresponds in quantum mechanics the existence of a finite probability that the atom is in an excited state. In practice, usually only the absorption in the K-shell and in the L-shell is of importance, and this absorption will hardly be influenced by excitation or ionization of the outer shells. Ionization of the K-shell will have a certain influence on absorption in the L-shell, but it is hardly to be expected that the probability of ionization of the K-shell in a radioactive disintegration will be comparable to unity. A calculation of this probability would certainly not be devoid of interest, but for the theory of internal conversion the result would be of little importance.

The calculation of the ratio of the probabilities of the two processes (emission of radiation and internal conversion) has to be carried out for only one orientation of the electric moment and one orientation of the magnetic moment, since it is clear that the result must be independent of this orientation. It is not so evident that in the case of electric quadrupole radiation this ratio for a field φ^m, $\mathbf{A}^m$ also has a value independent of m and therefore also has this same value when the field is given by $\sum c_m \varphi^m$, $\sum c_m \mathbf{A}^m$ with arbitrary c_m. The simplest way of proving this result is to consider first the case in which a nucleus carries out a transition $i = 2 \rightarrow i = 0$; in this case it can easily be shown that the probability of emission of a quantum and the probability of internal conversion are both independent of m; and the same will hold for their ratio.

Finally, it must be shown that the total probability of internal conversion in a field that is a superposition of a dipole and a quadrupole field is equal to the sum of the probabilities belonging to these fields separately. This can be proved by a group-theoretical argument. The dipole field and the quadrupole field will transform according to different irreducible representations of the group of three-dimensional rotations.

The required result is now a special case of the following theorem. Let O_1^λ, O_2^μ be two sets of operators, transforming according to nonequivalent irreducible representations of the rotation group;

let Ψ_j^m; $(-j \leq m \leq j)$ be $2j + 1$ wave functions belonging to an angular momentum j; let $\Psi_{j'}^{m'}$ be $(-j' \leq m \leq j')$, $2j' + 1$ wave functions belonging to an angular momentum j'; then we have:

$$\sum_{m,m'} \left| \int \Psi_{j'}^{*m'} (O_1^\lambda + O_2^\mu) \Psi_j^m \right|^2$$

$$= \sum_{m,m'} \left| \int \Psi_j^{*m'} O_1^\lambda \Psi_j^m \right|^2 + \sum_{m,m'} \left| \int \Psi_{j'}^{*m'} O_2^\mu \Psi_j^m \right|^2.$$

23. The calculations of Hulme, Taylor, and Mott and of Fisk and Taylor

In order to calculate the probability of internal conversion one has to introduce simplifying assumptions. In their calculations, the authors whose work is discussed here treated this as a one-electron problem, and described the states of the electron by using the wave functions for a Coulomb field of force. For heavy nuclei it is to be expected that this approximation will be permissible for the initial state, since the interaction of the electrons will be small compared to the interaction with the nucleus.

As to the final state, one might expect that a fairly accurate approximation will be obtained by using the wave functions for an electron moving in a Coulomb field screened off by the other electrons. The neglect of screening will have no appreciable influence when the energy of the final state is large ($\gg Z^2\alpha^2mc^2$), but it would be desirable to examine its influence for smaller energy values.

It must not be forgotten, however, that when the wave functions for a Coulomb field are being used, the calculations are still extremely cumbersone. Since the energy in the final state is usually large, and since the problem is chiefly of interest for heavy nuclei, it is necessary to use relativistic wave functions. Indeed the non-relativistic calculations of Swirles (*39*) lead to results that differ appreciably from those found by Hulme. On the other hand, the author (*10*) has tried to solve the problem by using the first term of their asymptotic expansion to approximate wave functions. Although it may be proved that this procedure will lead to correct results in the limit $(\hbar v/mc^2) \to \infty$, Hulme's calculations have shown that for energies occurring in actual applications this approximation leads to entirely erroneous results. So it is necessary to use the exact expression for the wave function of the final state. The integration over the angles ϑ, φ can be carried out without difficulty. The radial wave function for the final state is a so-called $W_{k,m}$ function, and the radial integral will be of the form

$$\int W_{k,m}\, e^{(-a+ib)r}\, r^s dr.$$

Integrals of this type can be expressed in terms of hypergeometric functions, and (after some reductions) these must be calculated numerically.

Another possibility would be to compute the wave function for the final state numerically and to determine the matrix elements by means of numerical integration. If one had at one's disposition a set of tables for these wave functions in the continuous spectrum, one would also be able to solve a number of other problems. For small values of r the wave functions can be determined by means of a power series, for larger values (12.5) must be integrated numerically and for still larger values a W-K-B solution of (12.11) and (12.12) must be fitted to these numerical values. An advantage of this numerical method is that screening can easily be taken into account.*

24. Results of the calculations and comparison with experiment

We shall now give a short survey of the results obtained by the authors mentioned. Since it is extremely difficult for an outsider to judge the reliability of the experimental data, no attempt will be made at a critical discussion of these data. For some of the hard γ-rays of RaC ($\hbar\nu > mc^2$) the experimental values of the coefficient of internal conversion—that is, the ratio (number of light quanta)/ (number of secondary electrons)—are in satisfactory agreement with the values calculated for dipole radiation, whereas for the other rays these coefficients are much larger and are in agreement with the theoretical results for quadrupole radiation. There is only one transition for which the data are neither in agreement with the theoretical results for dipole radiation nor with those for quad-

---

* Extensive calculations of this type have been carried out [see M. E. Rose, *Internal Conversion Coefficients* (North-Holland Publishing Co., Amsterdam, 1958)].

rupole radiation—the transition with energy 1.416×10^6 ev. The corresponding γ-ray has never been observed, and it seems possible that the transition is a transition $0 \to 0$. In that case emission of radiation is impossible, and the transition would be entirely due to the "interior" part of the interaction, which was neglected in the foregoing calculations.

For the soft γ-rays of RaB the conversion coefficients are larger than those calculated for quadrupole radiation but are smaller than those calculated for magnetic dipole radiation. They can be explained by assuming that the radiation is a superposition of quadrupole and magnetic dipole radiation (Taylor and Fisk (17)). We believe that one is justified in drawing the following conclusions: hard γ-rays are either dipole or quadrupole radiation; soft γ-rays consist, at least in part, of magnetic dipole radiation.

In our considerations the "interior" part of the interaction (that is, the interaction of the nucleus and the electronic charge and current that lie inside the nucleus) has been neglected. It is easily seen that this is permissible except for the transition mentioned above, provided that this interaction is not much larger than would be expected from the ordinary formalism of quantum mechanics.

For a number of years the opinion prevailed that it was impossible to explain the experimental facts without assuming such a large interaction, but the work of Hulme and the other author cited has proved this conclusion incorrect. Moreover, we must point out that the results concerning the hyperfine structure also indicate that abnormally large interior interactions do not exist.

Attempts have been made to use the knowledge obtained concerning the type of radiation of the different transitions for the construction of a scheme of energy levels in which i-values are assigned to the levels, but we will not dwell upon the results obtained in this way.

25. Some considerations on nuclear structure*

In this final section we shall put forward some considerations on

---

* Although these considerations are rather out of date, they are reproduced here in their original form. It may amuse today's readers to note the kind of thinking that prevailed twenty-five years ago with regard to nuclei.

nuclear structure based on results that were obtained by the methods outlined in this paper.

From the investigation of the hyperfine structure of spectral lines, information is obtained concerning certain properties of the fundamental state of the nucleus: one can determine the angular momentum, the magnetic moment, and in some cases the quadrupole moment. As to the displacements that are found in the isotope effect and which are independent of f, since they cannot be ascribed to nuclear motion (such an interpretation will only be possible for light elements), they must be due to deviations from Coulomb's law. They may be described in terms of an effective nuclear radius, but no definite physical meaning can be given to that quantity, since it is not to be expected that the interaction can be described as the interaction of two charge densities; at present, however, any other hypothesis concerning this interaction is rather arbitrary.

Nevertheless, it is satisfactory that the effective radii for the different isotopes of one element increase with increasing atomic weight. Samarium (*38*) is of special interest in that the isotope-shifts depend irregularly on the atomic weight, and one can infer that an irregularity must exist in the structure of the nuclei.

Let us now consider the values of the angular momentum derived from the study of hyperfine structure (and partly from the study of band spectra). The most essential feature of these values is that they do not contradict the assumption that the nucleus is built of protons and neutrons, both particles having a spin of $\frac{1}{2}$. There seem to exist certain other regularities, but no general rules for predicting the angular momentum of an arbitrary nucleus can be given.

No satisfactory theory has been given for the values of the magnetic moments. Attempts have been made to arrive at an understanding of these values in terms of a vector model, but the number of theoretical possibilities is so large and the values of the moments are so uncertain that we do not believe that definite results can be obtained in this way.

Let us now consider some of the light nuclei in more detail. The simplest nucleus is the proton. The angular momentum determined from the band spectrum is $\frac{1}{2}$. The magnetic moment was determined by Stern and Frisch (*18*) and by Estermann (*13*), as well as by

Rabi, Kellog, and Zacharias (*31*) by means of measurements on atomic or molecular beams. The factor γ is not 2 (as would follow from Dirac's theory) but about thrice as large. It follows, then, that the proton cannot be described by Dirac's equation. This is probably connected with Fermi's theory, according to which a proton can be transformed into a neutron, a positron, and a neutrino.

The deuteron (heavy hydrogen nucleus) consists of a proton and a neutron. The angular momentum is 1. This value can be explained by assuming that there is no orbital angular momentum and that the spins of proton and neutron are parallel. The magnetic moment can be estimated from the influence of paramagnetic gases on the velocity of the transformation ortho-hydrogen→para-hydrogen. One obtains the value $\gamma = 0.7$. This leads to the supposition that the neutron has a negative magnetic moment (that is, a moment opposite to the angular momentum). Various hypotheses have been made concerning the neutron-proton interaction. Of these the hypothesis of Majorana (*27*) has been most successful in explaining the values of the nuclear binding energies. According to Majorana the interaction is of the exchange type and is independent of the orientation of the spins. The only interaction between the spins would then be the magnetic interaction. Because of this magnetic interaction the state with parallel spins would be the state of lowest energy, but there would exist another state in which the spins oppose one another. An estimation of the energy difference of these states leads to a value of 10^4 or 10^5 ev.* From an experimental point of view, no objection can be made to this value, but theoretical investigations of Weizsäcker (*42*) and a discussion of the capture of neutrons by protons presented by Fermi (*15*) seem to show that the exchange forces are not completely independent of the orientation of the spins, with the result that there will exist a spin-spin interaction that is much larger than the magnetic interaction. However this may be, the structure of the deuteron does not offer essential difficulties. For the α-particle $i = 0$; it can be interpreted as a highly symmetrical system of two protons and two neutrons.

Let us now consider Li_6 and N_{14}. For these nuclei $i = 1$; and the

---

* This conclusion was incorrect. See the author's paper on the deuteron, quoted in the Preface.

magnetic moment is certainly small. This would be in agreement with the view that these nuclei consist of a deuteron and a number of α-particles (one or three). According to Schüler (47) the magnetic moment of Li_6 is of the same order of magnitude as that of the deuteron, but Bacher (1) gives $\gamma < 0.2$ for N_{14}, which means that an application of the vector model in its usual form is impossible. Schüler and Schmidt have tried to explain the situation by assuming that the magnetic moment of the proton depends on the mass of the nucleus. Although it cannot be excluded a priori that one might arrive at a satisfactory description of magnetic moments by means of a vector model with varying moment of the proton, one must not forget that such a vector model would be fundamentally different from the usual one; moreover, in the author's opinion such a satisfactory theory of magnetic moments has not yet been given, nor does a discussion of other magnetic moments lead to a convincing argument against Weizsäcker's conclusion, according to which the spin-spin and spin-orbit interactions in the nucleus are so large that an application of the usual vector model is out of the question.

We will now consider the large positive quadrupole moments of Cp and Eu. For Cp we have $(\overline{3z^2 - r^2}) \approx 5.6 \times 10^{-24}$. If we assume a value of 0.7×10^{-12} for the radius of the nucleus, and if we take into account that for one particle the mean value of $3 \cos^2 \vartheta - 1$ is certainly smaller than 2 (actually this value can only be approximated by making very improbable assumptions), then one is led to the conclusion that the quadrupole moment cannot possibly be due to one proton. Thus it is necessary to assume that it is caused by a group of particles. It might even be that the nucleus as a whole has a prolate shape and that the nucleus as a whole is rotating about its major axis. In this connection there may be some point in remarking that for heavy nuclei the rotational energy estimated by means of the elementary formula $E = \hbar^2/2I$ (I = moment of inertia) is small compared to the binding energy. In any case the existence of large quadrupole moments seems to offer an argument in favor of the idea that the nucleus must be treated as a whole and that its properties are not determined by the behavior of one particle.

We turn now to the discussion of the results obtained in the investigation of internal conversion that were mentioned in Section 24.

If it were possible to speak of an excited state of one proton or of one neutron (or perhaps of one α-particle) then one should expect the radiation to be almost exclusively dipole radiation. Quadrupole radiation would only be emitted with a measurable intensity in those cases in which a nucleus is in an excited state from which transitions by means of dipole radiation are forbidden by the selection rules, and the frequent occurrence of quadrupole radiation would force us to make very artificial assumptions concerning the scheme of levels. We are inclined to believe that the existence of quadrupole radiation is a consequence of the very strong binding forces between the particles in the nucleus. Quadrupole radiation would be emitted by a rotating nucleus with a large quadrupole moment as well as by a vibrating nuclear "drop."

Finally, it is of interest to consider in some detail the possibility that magnetic dipole radiation will occur. In atomic spectra magnetic dipole radiation will rarely occur. In zero approximation this radiation will always vanish. It can only occur as a consequence of spin-orbit interaction.

But let us now consider the two hypothetical states of the deuteron with $i = 1$ and $i = 0$. In either case a transition with emission of magnetic dipole radiation is possible. Fermi (15) has explained the large cross section for the capture of neutrons by protons by assuming that in this process magnetic dipole radiation is emitted. This explanation is possible only when the spin-spin interaction is not exclusively magnetic. An argument for the existence of spin-spin interaction may be derived from a discussion of the data on the elastic scattering of neutrons by protons. Fermi has even succeeded in deriving a definite value for the capture cross section that is in satisfactory agreement with experiment.

More generally, in any transition that corresponds to a change of direction of a spin magnetic dipole, radiation will be emitted. If the transition corresponds to a change of the relative orientation of a spin and an orbital momentum, the radiation field will be a superposition of magnetic dipole radiation and quadrupole radiation. The results of Weizsäcker and Fermi seem to show that in such transitions a rather large amount of energy may be emitted.

Thus we conclude that the assumption that the very large conversion coefficients for the soft γ-rays of RaC are due to magnetic dipole radiation is probably correct.* On the other hand the existence of these large coefficients offers a further argument in favor of the existence of rather large spin-spin and spin-orbit interactions.

Since our paper was written there has appeared an article by Bohr (44) on nuclear structure. It seems to us that our speculations concerning the structure of the nucleus fit in very well with the general scheme put forward by Bohr.

---

* Hulme, Mott, Oppenheimer, and Taylor arrived at a similar conclusion (*Proc. Roy. Soc.* London. Ser. A. **155**:315, 1936).

References

1. R. F. BACHER, *Phys. Rev.*, **43**:1001, 1933.
2. H. BETHE, *Handbuch der Physik*, 2e Aufl. 24¹, Berlin, 1933.
3. H. BETHE and E. FERMI, *Z. Physik*, **77**:296, 1932.
4. G. BREIT, *Phys. Rev.* **42**:348, 1932.
5. G. BREIT and J. ROSENTHAL, *Phys. Rev.*, **41**:459, 1932.
6. G. BREIT and L. A. WILLS, *Phys. Rev.*, **44**:470, 1933.
7. H. C. BRINKMAN, *Acad. Proefschrift*, Utrecht, 1932.
8. H. CASIMIR, *Physica*, **2**:719, 1935.
9. H. CASIMIR, *Z. Physik*, **77**:811, 1932.
10. H. CASIMIR, *Nature*, **126**:953, 1930.
11. E. M. CONDON and G. H. SHORTLEY, *Theory of Atomic Spectra,* Cambridge University Press, 1935.
12. M. F. CRAWFORD and N. S. GRACE, *Phys. Rev.*, **47**:536, 1935.
13. I. ESTERMANN and O. STERN, *Z. Physik*, **85**:17, 1933.
14. L. and A. FARKAS, *Nature*, **135**:372, 1935.
15. E. FERMI, *Phys. Rev.*, **48**:570, 1935.
16. E. FERMI and E. SEGRE, *Z. Physik*, **82**:729, 1933.
17. J. B. FISK and H. M. TAYLOR, *Proc. Roy. Soc.* London. Ser. A, **146**:178, 1935.
18. R. FRISCH and O. STERN, *Z. Physik*, **85**:4, 1933.
20. S. A. GOUDSMIT, *Phys. Rev.*, **43**:636, 1933.
21. S. A. GOUDSMIT, *Phys. Rev.*, **37**:663, 1931.
22. S. A. GOUDSMIT and R. F. BACHER, *Phys. Rev.*, **43**:894, 1933.
23. P. GÜTTINGER and W. PAULI, *Z. Physik*, **67**:743, 1931.
24. W. HEISENBERG, *Ann. Physik* (5), **9**:338, 1931.
25. H. R. HULME, *Proc. Roy. Soc.* London. Ser. A, **138**:643, 1932.
26. H. A. KRAMERS, *Proc. Roy. Acad. Amsterdam*, **34**:965, 1931.
27. E. MAJORANA, *Z. Physik*, **82**:132, 1933.
28. CHR. MOLLER, *Z. Physik*, **70**:786, 1931.
29. CHR. MOLLER, *Proc. Roy. Soc.* London. Ser. A, **152**:481, 1935.
30. F. PASCHEN, *Sitz. Ber.* Berlin, 456, 1934.
31. I. RABI, J. R. M. KELLOG, and J. R. ZACHARIAS, *Phys. Rev.*, **46**:157, 1934.
32. H. N. RUSSELL and A. S. KING, *Phys. Rev.*, **46**:1023, 1934.
33. H. SCHÜLER, *Z. Physik*, **42**:487, 1927; **66**:431, 1930.
34. H. SCHÜLER and E. JONES, *Z. Physik*, **77**:802, 1932.
35. H. SCHÜLER and TH. SCHMIDT, *Z. Physik*, **94**:457, 1935.
36. H. SCHÜLER and TH. SCHMIDT, *Z. Physik*, **95**:265, 1935.
37. H. SCHÜLER and TH. SCHMIDT, *Phys. Z.*, **36**:812, 1935.
38. H. SCHÜLER and TH. SCHMIDT, *Z. Physik*, **92**:148, 1934.
39. B. SWIRLES, *Proc. Roy. Soc.* London. Ser. A, **116**:491; 1927; **121**:447, 1928.
40. H. M. TAYLOR and N. F. MOTT, *Proc. Roy. Soc.* London. Ser. A, **138**:666, 1932.
41. H. M. TAYLOR and N. F. MOTT, *Proc. Roy. Soc.* London. Ser. A, **142**:215, 1933.
42. C. F. V. WEIZSÄCKER, *Phys. Z.*, **36**:779, 1935.
43. H. WOLFE, *Phys. Rev.*, **41**:443, 1932.
44. N. BOHR, *Nature*, **137**:344, 1936.
45. H. R. HULME, *Proc. Roy. Soc.* London. Ser. A, **154**:487, 1936.
46. H. SCHÜLER and TH. SCHMIDT, *Z. Physik*, **98**:239, 1935.
47. H. SCHÜLER and TH. SCHMIDT, *Z. Physik*, **99**:285, 1936.
48. H. SCHÜLER and TH. SCHMIDT, *Z. Physik*, **99**:717, 1936.
49. H. SCHÜLER and TH. SCHMIDT, *Z. Physik*, **100**:113, 1936.

Multipole Expansions

1. Notations: addition theorem

Here we shall investigate the field produced by a charge density ρ and a current density i enclosed in a sphere of radius R and varying periodically with the time factor $\exp(-ikct)$. We have

$$\frac{\partial \rho}{\partial t} + \operatorname{div} i = 0,$$

or

$$ikc\rho + \operatorname{div} \mathbf{i} = 0.$$

Since $Y_l^m(\vartheta, \varphi)$ with $-l \leq m \leq l$ are normalized surface harmonics, we have

$$Y_l^m = (Y_l^{-m})^*,$$

$$\iint Y_l^m(\vartheta, \varphi)\, Y_{l'}^{-m'}(\vartheta, \varphi) \sin \vartheta \, d\vartheta \, d\varphi = 4\pi \delta_{ll'} \delta_{mm'}.$$

The corresponding polynomials are T_l^m:

$$T_l^m = Y_l^m r^l.$$

Further, we shall write

$$\Pi_l^m(\mathbf{r}) = h_l(kr)\, Y_l^m(\vartheta, \varphi),$$

and

$$\Pi_{1l}^m(\mathbf{r}') = j_l(kr')\, Y_l^m(\vartheta', \varphi'),$$

with

$$j_n(x) = \left(\frac{\pi}{2x}\right)^{1/2} J_{n+1/2}(u),$$

and

$$h_n(u) = \left(\frac{\pi}{2u}\right)^{1/2} H_{n+(1/2)}^{(1)}(u).$$

There exists the following addition theorem, the general form of which is at once evident from group-theoretical arguments, although the determination of numerical factors requires some further analysis:

$$\frac{e_{ik|\mathbf{r}-\mathbf{r}'|}}{|\mathbf{r} - \mathbf{r}'|} = ik \sum_{n,\,m} \Pi_n^m(r)\, \Pi_{1n}^{-m}(r') \qquad (A\text{-}1)$$

which is valid for $r > r'$.

2. Vector harmonics

Consider $3(2l + 1)$ vector fields $\mathbf{F}_{s,\,l}^m$ with $s = 1,\ 2,\ 3$ and $-l \leq m \leq l$,

$$\mathbf{F}_{s,\,l}^m = \mathbf{a}(s)T_l^m,$$

where $\mathbf{a}(s)$ is the unit vector in the direction of the s-axis. Any vector field whose components are homogeneous polynomials of degree l and which satisfies Laplace's equation is a linear combination of the $\mathbf{F}_{s,\,l}^m$.

If these vector fields are rotated around the origin, they transform according to the direct product

$$D_1 \times D_l;$$

inversion gives a factor $(-)^{l+1}$.

Let us now consider the expressions

$$\nabla T_{l+1}^m, \qquad\qquad\qquad (A\text{-}2)$$

$$r^2\, \nabla T_{l-1}^m - (2l - 1)\mathbf{r}T_{l-1}^m, \qquad\qquad (A\text{-}3)$$

$$\operatorname{curl}(\mathbf{r}T_l^m). \qquad\qquad\qquad (A\text{-}4)$$

It is easy to show that the components of each of these fields satisfy Laplace's equation and that they are homogeneous polynomials of degree l. Hence these vector fields are linear combinations of the $\mathbf{F}_{s,\,l}^m$. Moreover, since they are derived by invariant operations from quantities transforming as D_{l+1}, D_{l-1} and D_l, respectively, it follows that they transform according to these same representations and therefore are linearly independent. Since the total number of components of (*A-2*), (*A-3*), and (*A-4*) is $3(2l + 1)$, we have solved the problem of finding those linear combinations of the $\mathbf{F}_{s,\,l}^{m}$ for which $D_1 \times D_l$ is split into its irreducible constituents, and simultaneously we have proved that these constituents are D_{l+1}, D_l, and D_{l-1}, which is in agreement with general theorems of group theory. Under inversion all three fields are multiplied by $(-)^{l+1}$. For (*A-2*) and (*A-3*) this is evident; for (*A-4*) one has to bear in mind that, under an inversion, curl changes into $-$curl.

The following properties are worthy of note. If $f(r)$ is an arbitrary function, then

$$f(r) \text{ curl } (\mathbf{r}T_l^m) = \text{curl } [\mathbf{r}T_l^m f(r)].$$

This is the most general form of a vector field transforming as D_l with inversion factor $(-)^{l+1}$. Further, we have

$$\mathbf{r} \cdot \text{curl } [\mathbf{r}T_l^m f(r)] = 0,$$

$$\mathbf{r} \cdot \text{curl curl } [\mathbf{r}T_l^m f(r)] = l(l + 1)T_l^m f(r).$$

This identity follows from the fact that T_l^m is a homogeneous polynomial of degree l that satisfies Laplace's equation.

The most general vector field transforming as D_l with inversion factor $(-)^l$ is

$$\mathbf{F} = h(r)\, r^2\, \nabla T_l^m - g(r)\, (2l + 1)\, \mathbf{r}T_l^m,$$

where $h(r)$ and $g(r)$ are arbitrary functions of r. If, however, $\mathbf{F}$ has to satisfy the additional condition div $\mathbf{F} = 0$, this can always be written as

$$\mathbf{F} = \text{curl curl } (\mathbf{r}T_l^m f(r)).$$

3. Solutions of Maxwell's equations

For $r > R$ we have

$$\text{curl } \mathbf{H} + ik\mathbf{E} = 0,$$

$$\text{curl } \mathbf{E} - ik\mathbf{H} = 0.$$

These equations are invariant under rotation, and it follows from the completeness theorem of irreducible representations that any solution is a superposition of solutions that transform according to irreducible representations.

If $\mathbf{E}$ transforms as D_l, $\mathbf{H}$ also transforms as D_l; but if the inversion factor of $\mathbf{E}$ is $(-)^l$, that of $\mathbf{H}$ is $(-)^{l+1}$, and vice versa. Hence there are two types of irreducible fields:

(1) When $\mathbf{E}$ transforms as D_l with an inversion factor $(-)^{l+1}$, then

$$\mathbf{E} = \text{curl } (\mathbf{r}\, f(r)\, T_l^m),$$

and

$$\mathbf{H} = \frac{1}{ik} \text{ curl curl } (\mathbf{r}\, f(r)\, T_l^m),$$

from which it follows that

$$\mathbf{E} \cdot \mathbf{r} = 0,$$

$$\mathbf{H} \cdot \mathbf{r} = \frac{l(l+1)}{ik} f(r)\, T_l^m.$$

It follows from Maxwell's equations and from the radiation condition at infinity that we can write

$$f(r)\, T_l^m = Cik\Pi_l^m.$$

We shall denote these fields (for $C = 1$) by

$$_M\mathbf{E}_l^m, \qquad _M\mathbf{H}_l^m.$$

These are called magnetic 2^l-pole fields.

(2) When $\mathbf{H}$ transforms as D_l with an inversion factor of $(-)^{l+1}$, then

$$\mathbf{H} = \text{curl } (\mathbf{r}\, f(r)\, T_l^m),$$

and

$$\mathbf{E} = -\frac{1}{ik} \text{ curl curl } (\mathbf{r}\, f(r)\, T_l^m),$$

from which it follows that

$$\mathbf{r} \cdot \mathbf{H} = 0, \qquad \mathbf{r} \cdot \mathbf{E} = -\frac{l(l+1)}{ik} f(r)\, T_l^m. \qquad (A\text{-}5)$$

Again,

$$f(r)\, T_l^m = Cik\Pi_l^m.$$

Such fields are called electric 2^l-pole fields, and will be denoted (for $C = 1$) as

$$_E\mathbf{E}_l^m, \qquad _E\mathbf{H}_l^m.$$

The most general solution can therefore be written as

$$\mathbf{E} = \sum a_l^m \,_E\mathbf{E}_l^m + \sum b_l^m \,_M\mathbf{E}_l^m, \tag{A-6}$$
$$\mathbf{H} = \sum a_l^m \,_E\mathbf{H}_l^m + \sum b_l^m \,_M\mathbf{H}_l^m,$$

and the total energy radiated per unit time is given by

$$P = \frac{1}{2} c \sum_{l,\,m} l(l+1)\,(|a_l^m|^2 + |b_l^m|^2).$$

4. Source representation

It follows from (A-5) and (A-6) that

$$\mathbf{r} \cdot \mathbf{E} = -\sum_{l,\,m} a_l^m l(l+1)\Pi_l^m,$$

$$\mathbf{r} \cdot \mathbf{H} = \sum_{l,\,m} b_l^m l(l+1)\Pi_l^m.$$

Since $\mathbf{r} \cdot \mathbf{E}$ and $\mathbf{r} \cdot \mathbf{H}$ are thus seen to be solutions of d'Alembert's equation outside the sphere of radius R, it is reasonable to look for an equation for these quantities for *all r*.

It is easily derived from Maxwell's equations that

$$\Delta\mathbf{H} + k^2\mathbf{H} = -\frac{4\pi}{c}\,\text{curl}\,\mathbf{i}.$$

Further, if we define

$$\mathbf{F} = \mathbf{E} - \frac{4\pi}{ikc}\,\mathbf{i},$$

then

$$\text{div}\,\mathbf{F} = 0,$$

$$\Delta\mathbf{F} + k^2\mathbf{F} = \frac{4\pi}{ikc}\,\text{curl curl}\,\mathbf{i}.$$

Since

$$(\Delta + k^2)\,(\mathbf{r}\cdot v) = r\,(\Delta v + k^2 v)$$

for any divergence-free vector v, we have

$$(\Delta + k^2)\,(\mathbf{r}\cdot \mathbf{H}) = -\frac{4\pi}{c}\,(\mathbf{r}\cdot \mathrm{curl}\,\mathbf{i}),$$

$$(\Delta + k^2)\,(\mathbf{r}\cdot \mathbf{F}) = \frac{4\pi}{ikc}\,(\mathbf{r}\cdot \mathrm{curl}\,\mathrm{curl}\,\mathbf{i}).$$

We therefore have

$$\mathbf{r}\cdot \mathbf{H} = \frac{1}{c}\int (\mathbf{r}'\cdot \mathrm{curl}'\,\mathbf{i})\,\frac{e^{ik\,|\mathbf{r}-\mathbf{r}'|}}{|\mathbf{r}-\mathbf{r}'|}\,dV'.$$

and

$$\mathbf{r}\cdot \mathbf{E} = \frac{4\pi}{ikc}\,(\mathbf{r}\cdot \mathbf{i}) - \frac{1}{ikc}\int (\mathbf{r}'\cdot \mathrm{curl}'\,\mathrm{curl}'\,\mathbf{i})\,\frac{e^{ik\,|\mathbf{r}-\mathbf{r}'|}}{|\mathbf{r}-\mathbf{r}'|}\,dV'.$$

Using the expansion $(A\text{-}1)$ and equating coefficients we find

$$a_l^m = -\frac{1}{c}\,\frac{1}{l(l+1)}\int \mathbf{i}(\mathbf{r}')\,\mathrm{curl}'\,\mathrm{curl}'\,(\mathbf{r}'\Pi_{1l}^{-m})\,dV',$$

$$b_l^m = \frac{ik}{c}\,\frac{1}{l(l+1)}\int \mathbf{i}(\mathbf{r}')\,\mathrm{curl}'\,(\mathbf{r}'\Pi_{1l}^{-m})\,dV'.$$

5. Vector potential

In order to calculate transitions induced by the radiation field we have to know the vector potential. Since

$$\mathrm{curl}\,\mathbf{E} = ik\mathbf{H},$$

we can set

$$\mathbf{A} = -\frac{1}{ik}\,\mathbf{E}.$$

This is the vector potential with the gauge condition $\Phi = 0$; and for $r > R$ we have div $\mathbf{A} = 0$, which is most commonly used in the more elementary forms of quantum electrodynamics.

In classical theory, and also in relativistic considerations, however, one usually determines the gauge by the condition

$$\text{div } \mathbf{A}_1 - ik\Phi_1 = 0,$$

from which it follows that

$$\Phi_1 = \int \rho(\mathbf{r}') \, \frac{e_{ik|\mathbf{r}-\mathbf{r}'|}}{|\mathbf{r} - \mathbf{r}'|} \, dV'$$

and

$$\mathbf{A}_1 = \mathbf{A} - \frac{1}{ik} \, \nabla\Phi_1.$$

Since Φ_1 can be expanded as

$$\Phi_1 = ik \sum \Pi_n^m \int \rho\Pi_{1n}^{-m} \, dV' = ik \sum c_n^m \Pi_n^m,$$

we find that the field corresponding to the magnetic multipole l, m is described by

$$\mathbf{A}_1 = -\frac{1}{ik} \, b_l^m \, \text{curl } (\mathbf{r}\Pi_l^m).$$

But for the *electric* multipole we have

$$\mathbf{A}_1 = \frac{1}{ik} \, a_l^m \, \text{curl curl } (\mathbf{r}\Pi_l^m) - c_l^m \, \nabla\Pi_l^m,$$

$$\Phi_1 = ikc_l^m \Pi_l^m.$$

Magnetic Octupole Moment of a Nucleus*

Summary

The influence of a nuclear magnetic octupole moment on the hyperfine structure of spectra is discussed. It is shown that an effect of the order of magnitude deduced by Tolansky cannot be explained by any model, which is not entirely in disagreement with present day views on the nucleus.

1. Introduction

It is now well known, that the analysis of hyperfine structure of atomic spectra may give information on three properties of the fundamental state of the nucleus. The fact that the nucleus is not a point charge but has a finite radius does not lead to a splitting of terms corresponding to one isotope, but it does lead to a difference in term value between different isotopes, the so-called isotope shift. The splitting of terms corresponding to different relative orientations of the atomic angular momentum and the nuclear angular momentum is mainly due to the interaction of the electron and the nuclear magnetic (dipole) moment. This leads to an energy aC, where C is the Landé cosine,

$$C = f(j + 1) - i(i + 1) - j(j + 1),$$

and the hyperfine structure will follow the so-called interval rule. Deviations from the interval rule may be due to interaction with neighboring terms; if this is not the case they are caused by the electric quadrupole moment of the nucleus. The splittings due to this effect can be represented by $bC(C + 1)$. Some time ago

---

* H. B. G. Casimir and G. Karreman (reprinted from *Physica*, 9:494, 1942).

Tolansky* published results on the spectrum of iodine; he arrived at the conclusion that, on the one hand, for several terms perturbation by neighboring terms is out of the question, whereas, on the other hand, the separations cannot be represented by a formula $aC + bC(C + 1)$. Therefore Tolansky has used an expression

$$aC + bC(C + 1) + c\left(C^3 + 4C^2 + \frac{4}{5}\, C \right)$$

to describe his results. An interaction energy containing C^3 can be explained in terms of a magnetic octupole moment of the nucleus; but there is one serious objection to such an interpretation. One should expect the ratio between dipole and octupole interaction to be of the order of magnitude (nuclear radius/atomic radius)², which is an extremely small quantity, and it was therefore always considered evident that higher multipoles will never lead to measurable effects. One of the authors had the opportunity to point out this difficulty to Dr. Tolansky, who has given due attention to this question in his paper. Nevertheless, we still believe that it may be of some interest to present the theory in more detail and to calculate more accurately the value of octupole moment required to obtain an effect of the order of magnitude found by Tolansky. The mathematical treatment is analogous to that given in the text.

2. *General formulas*

The general formula for the magnetic interaction between nucleus and electron is

$$\Delta W = -\frac{1}{c} \int (\mathbf{A} \cdot \mathbf{i})\, d\tau, \qquad (B\text{-}1)$$

where $\mathbf{A}$ is the vector potential of the field due to the atomic electrons and $\mathbf{i}$ is the current density in the fundamental state of the nucleus and where the integration is carried out over the volume of the nucleus, which we will assume to be limited by a sphere of radius R_k. We introduce the nuclear magnetization $\mathbf{m}$ by the equation

$$\mathbf{i} = c \operatorname{curl} \mathbf{m}$$

---

* S. Tolansky, *Proc. Roy. Soc.* Ser. A, **170**:214, 1939.

and the further condition $\mathbf{m} = 0$ for $R > R_k$. Then $(B\text{-}1)$ may be transformed into

$$\Delta W = - \int (\mathbf{H} \cdot \mathbf{m})\, d\tau.$$

We expand $\mathbf{H}$ into a power series

$$H_l = (H_l)_0 + \sum_k (\partial_k H_l)_0\, x_k + \frac{1}{2} \sum_{j,k} (\partial_i \partial_k H_l)_0\, x_i x_k + \cdots.$$

The first term leads to the usual expression

$$\Delta W_0 = - \sum_l (H_l)_0 \int m_l\, d\tau = - \mathbf{H}_0 \cdot \boldsymbol{\mu}.$$

The second term is zero for reasons of symmetry, and the term which interests us here is given by

$$\Delta W_2 = - \frac{1}{2} \sum_{i,k,l} (\partial_i \partial_k H_l)_0 \int (m_l x_i x_k)\, d\tau. \qquad (B\text{-}2)$$

This may be transformed into a term

$$- \frac{1}{6} \sum_l (\Delta H_l)_0 \int m_l r^2\, d\tau,$$

which gives a slight correction to the dipole interaction and an expression

$$- \sum_{m,l} [Y_2^m(\partial)\, H_l]_0 \int Y_2^{-m}(x)\, m_l\, d\tau, \qquad (B\text{-}3)$$

where the Y_2^m are harmonic polynomials. The expressions $Y_2^m(\partial)H_l$ do not transform as irreducible representations of the rotation group, but by taking suitable linear combinations we can obtain expressions that transform as spherical harmonics of degrees 3, 2, and 1 respectively. Of these the two latter possibilities lead to slight corrections to the dipole and quadrupole interactions that do not interest us here, and we are left with an expression

$$\Delta W_{\mathrm{Oct}} = a \sum_m Q_3^m(\partial, \mathbf{H}) \int Q_3^{-m}(x, \mathbf{m})\, d\tau,$$

where a is a constant and where the $Q_3^m(\partial, \mathbf{H})$ are polynomials of second degree in ∂ and first degree in H_l, which transform as spherical harmonics of the third degree. By transforming *(B-2)* to the form *(B-3)*, and by introducing the quantities $H_x \pm iH_y$ and $m_x \pm im_y$, there will arise a term

$$- \frac{1}{16} [(\partial_x + i\partial_y)^2 (H_x + iH_y)]_0 \int (x - iy)^2 (m_x - im_y) \, d\tau.$$

But this is already an expression of the type

$$aQ_3^3(\partial, \mathbf{H}) \int Q_3^{-3} (x, \mathbf{m}) \, d\tau,$$

thus we have

$$\Delta W_{\text{Oct}} = - \frac{1}{16} \sum_m Q_3^m (\partial, \mathbf{H}) \int Q_3^{-m} (x, \mathbf{m}) \, d\tau,$$

provided that

$$Q_3^3(\partial, \mathbf{H}) = (\partial_x + i\partial_y)^2 (H_x + iH_y),$$

$$Q_3^3(x, \mathbf{m}) = (x + iy)^2 (m_x + im_y),$$

and that the other Q_3^m are chosen in such a way that the Q_3^m transform under a rotation with a unitary representation of the rotation group. To derive the appropriate expressions for Q_3^0 we remark that

$$\int (x + iy)^2 (m_x + im_y) \, d\tau = - \frac{1}{3} \int (x + iy)^3 \operatorname{div} \mathbf{m} \, d\tau.$$

The harmonic polynomial with $m=0$ corresponding to $-\frac{1}{3}(x+iy)^3$ is given by $(2/3\sqrt{5})\,[2z^3 - 3z(x^2 + y^2)]$. Thus,

$$\int Q_3^0(x, \mathbf{m}) \, d\tau = \frac{2}{3\sqrt{5}} \int [2z^3 - 3z(x^2 + y^2)] \operatorname{div} \mathbf{m} \, d\tau$$

$$= \frac{2}{3\sqrt{5}} \int [(15z^2 - 3r^2) m_z - 6z(\mathbf{r} \cdot \mathbf{m})] \, d\tau.$$

The corresponding expression for $Q_3^0 (\partial, \mathbf{H})$ is

$$Q_3^0 (\partial, \mathbf{H}) = \frac{2}{\sqrt{5}} [(5\partial_z^2 - \Delta)H_z]_0.$$

According to a well-known theorem, we can write (as long as we restrict ourselves to matrix elements that are diagonal elements in j and i):

$$Q_3^m (\partial, \mathbf{H}) = q_H \, Y_3^m (J),$$

$$\int Q_3^m (x, \mathbf{m}) \, d\tau = q_m \, Y_3^m (I),$$

where q_H and q_m are independent of m and where the Y_3^m are harmonic polynomials in J_i and I_i, the angular momentum matrices. The constants q_H and q_m can be determined by calculating one matrix element for one definite value of m:

$$q_H \, Y_3^0(J)_{j, j,} = Q_3^0 (\partial, \mathbf{H})_{j, j,}$$

$$q_m \, Y_3^0 (I)_{i, i} = \int [Q_3^0 (x, \mathbf{m}) \, d\tau]_{i, i}.$$

The correct expression for $Y_3^0(J)$ is obtained by observing that it must be symmetrical in all three components:

$$Y_3^0(J) = 2J_z^3 - (J_z J_x^2 + J_x J_z J_x + J_x^2 J_z + J_z J_y^2 + J_y J_z J_y + J_y^2 J_z)$$
$$= 2J_z^3 - 3J_z (J_x^2 + J_y^2) + J_z.$$

It then follows that

$$Y_3^0 (J)_{j, j} = j(j - 1) (2j - 1).$$

The problem now is to calculate the eigenvalues of

$$\sum Y_3^m(J) \, Y_3^{-m}(I), \tag{B-4}$$

but here we can use a result of Kramers,[*] who has shown that these eigenvalues are given by

$$pQ_3 = p \left\{ - C^3 - 4C^2 - \frac{4}{5} C \left[- 3j(j + 1) \, i(i + 1) + j(j + 1) \right. \right.$$
$$\left. \left. + i(i + 1) + 3 \right] + 4i(i + 1) \, j(j + 1) \right\}.$$

To find the constant p we consider the special case $f = j + i$, for in that case it is evident that the eigenvalue of (B-4) is given by $i (i - 1) (2i - 1) j (j - 1) (2j - 1)$. If we assign Q_{max} the value of Q_3 in this special case, it follows that the eigenvalues of (B-4) are

$$\frac{i(i - 1) (2i - 1) \, j(j - 1) (2j - 1)}{Q_{max}} \, Q_3.$$

---

[*] H. A. Kramers, *Proc. Roy. Acad.* Amsterdam, **34**:965, 1931.

Thus our calculations may be summarized as follows:

$$\Delta W_{\text{Oct}} = -\frac{1}{48}\,\alpha\beta\,\frac{Q_3}{Q_{\max}},$$

where

$$\alpha = \frac{2}{\sqrt{5}}\,[(5\partial_z^2 H_z - \Delta H_z)_0]_{j,\,j}$$

and

$$\beta = \frac{2}{\sqrt{5}}\int [(5z^3 - 3zr^2)\,\text{div }\mathbf{m}\,\, d\tau]_{i,\,i}.$$

3. Calculation of α for a p-electron

In order to evaluate α, let us remark first of all that, from group theory, $\alpha \neq 0$ only for $j \geq 3/2$. Further we notice that

$$(\Delta H_z)_0 = -\,(\text{curl curl }\mathbf{H})_z = -\frac{4\pi}{c}\,[(\text{curl }\mathbf{i}_e)_z]_0,$$

where $\mathbf{i}_e$ is the current density of the electrons. Thus we see that this expression is zero for $l \geq 2$. In this respect the $p_{3/2}$-states are distinguished from other states. A $p_{3/2}$-state is exceptional for another reason: calculation of $(\partial^2 H_z/\partial z^2)$ will in general lead to an average value of $1/r^5$, but since this average does not exist for a p-state, we are faced with a situation analogous to that for an s-electron in the theory of dipole interaction. If an effect of the type postulated by Tolansky really exists, it must be due to the $(5p)$-electrons of iodine, and so we shall only evaluate α for one $p_{3/2}$-electron. For the orbital wave function in the state $m = 3/2$ we write

$$\Psi = \sqrt{\frac{3}{8\pi}}\,\sin\vartheta\,e^{i\phi}\,f(r) = \sqrt{\frac{3}{8\pi}}\,(x + iy)\,\frac{f}{r},$$

where f is normalized:

$$\int j^2\,r^2\,dr = 1.$$

The current density is the sum of two terms: an orbital current $\mathbf{i}_1$,

$$\mathbf{i}_1 = -\frac{e\hbar}{2mi}\,(\Psi^*\,\text{grad }\Psi - \Psi\,\text{grad }\Psi^*),$$

and a spin current

$$\mathbf{i}_2 = - \frac{e\hbar}{2m} \operatorname{curl} \Psi^* \Psi.$$

A simple calculation gives

$$(i_1)_x = \frac{3e\hbar}{8\pi m} \, yg,$$

$$(i_1)_y = - \frac{3e\hbar}{8\pi m} \, xg,$$

$$(i_2)_x = - \frac{3e\hbar}{8\pi m} \left[yg + \frac{1}{2} (x^2 + y^2) \frac{y}{r} g' \right],$$

$$(i_2)_y = + \frac{3e\hbar}{8\pi m} \left[xg + \frac{1}{2} (x^2 + y^2) \frac{x}{r} g' \right],$$

where

$$g = \left(\frac{f}{r} \right)^2.$$

It is a remarkable circumstance that for the *total* current, given by

$$(i_e)_x = - \frac{3e\hbar}{16\pi m} (x^2 + y^2) \frac{y}{r} g',$$

$$(i_e)_y = + \frac{3e\hbar}{16\pi m} (x^2 + y^2) \frac{x}{r} g',$$

curl $\mathbf{i} = 0$ for $r = 0$, such that the term containing ΔH_z gives no contribution after all. The calculation of $(\partial^2 H_z / \partial z^2)_0$ is easily carried out if we start from the formula

$$\left(\frac{\partial^2 H_z}{\partial z^2} \right)_0 = \frac{1}{c} \iiint \frac{\partial_z^2 (x i_{ey} - y i_{ex})}{r^3} \, dx \, dy \, dz.$$

we find that

$$\left(\frac{\partial^2 H_z}{\partial z^2} \right)_0 = - \frac{12}{35} \frac{e\hbar}{mc} (g0).$$

For the quantity $g(0)$ one can derive a "Goudsmit formula" by means of the method of Fermi (see Section 13), and we find

$$g(0) = \frac{2}{9} Z_i^3 \frac{2 Z_e^2}{n^{*3}} \frac{1}{a_0^5}.$$

Here Z_i and Z_e are the "interior" and "exterior" nuclear charge, n^* is the effective quantum number of the p-electron (hence Z_e^2/n^{*2} is the ionization energy in atomic units), and $a_0 = me^2/\hbar^2$.

4. Application to iodine

For a rigorous discussion of the iodine spectrum it would be necessary to study in some detail the coupling of the three $(5p)$-electrons in the *JII* spectrum, but for our present purpose it will be sufficient to remark that the value of $\partial^2 H_z/\partial z^2$ will be given by

$$-P \frac{12}{35} \frac{e\hbar}{mc} \frac{4 Z_i^3 Z_e^2}{9 n^{*3}} \frac{1}{a_0^5},$$

where P is a number of the order of magnitude one, which will certainly not surpass 3, since the three electrons cannot be simultaneously in the same $p_{3/2}$-state. To facilitate the discussion of the order of magnitude we set

$$\beta = \frac{2}{\sqrt{5}} \int (5z^3 - 3zr^2) \operatorname{div} \mathbf{m} \, d\tau = B \frac{e\hbar}{2Mc} R_k^2,$$

where B is now a dimensionless constant. For the energy we find:

$$\Delta W_{\text{Oct}} = \frac{4}{3} \frac{\sqrt{5}}{15} \left(\frac{m}{M} \right) \left(\frac{e\hbar}{2mc} \right)^2 \frac{1}{a_0^3} \left(\frac{R_k}{a_0} \right)^2 \frac{P Z_i^3 Z_e^2}{n^{*3}} \frac{Q_3}{Q_{\text{max}}} B.$$

Inserting numerical values, taking $(R_k/a_0) = 5 \times 10^{-3}$ (corresponding to $R_k = 10^{-12}$ cm), $Z_i = 50$, and assuming $j = 2$ (which is the case for Tolansky's terms) so that with $i = 5/2$, $Q_{\text{max}} = -72$ we find for the coefficient of C^3:

$$3 \times 10^{-6} \times \frac{Z_e^2}{n^{*3}} \times BP \times 10^{-3} \text{ cm}^{-1}.$$

An accurate estimate of Z_e^2/n^{*3} cannot easily be given, but by comparing the ionization energies of a p-electron in Cs II and in Br III and Cl III it is easily seen that it is safe to assume $Z_e^2/n^{*3} < 3$. Thus, if we write

$$c < 3 \times 10^{-5} B \times 10^{-3} \text{ cm}^{-1},$$

we make a very generous estimate. Since Tolansky's values were of the order $10^{-2} \times 10^{-3}$ cm^{-1} it follows that

$$B > 300.$$

5. *Discussion of B-value*

To arrive at an estimate of B let us first consider a total magnetic moment $\gamma e\hbar/2Mc$. If the magnetization is distributed homogeneously over a sphere we have $B = 0$. Two examples of distribution for which $B \neq 0$ are: $\mathbf{m} = 0$, except inside a flat disc, which gives

$$B_f = -\frac{2}{\sqrt{5}} \frac{3}{4} \gamma,$$

$\mathbf{m} = 0$, except inside a narrow cylinder, which gives

$$B_c = +\frac{2}{\sqrt{5}} 2\gamma.$$

Even in these rather extreme cases B is only of the order of magnitude one, and it is impossible to obtain a value greater than 300 with a few particles, unless we employ unreasonably large moments of the individual particles. Only if we assume that all particles inside the nucleus have octupole moments that add up—in contrast with the magnetic moments and angular momenta, which compensate each other—can we arrive at anything like the required value. As far as we can see, such a supposition would require a complete revision of existing ideas on nuclear structure, and the nature of the experimental evidence certainly does not warrant such a far-reaching conclusion. Another possibility may be mentioned. The large value of the magnetic moment of a proton can be ascribed to the virtual presence of a positron. In the same way, the value of B might be explained, but since this value is almost of the order of magnitude that might be expected for an electron, it seems impossible to reconcile such an explanation with the experimental fact that the magnetic dipole moment is always of the order $e\hbar/2Mc$. In these circumstances we are inclined to think that Tolansky's results must involve some unknown source of error in the analysis of the admittedly very intricate patterns.